Healthy Simple & Tasty

Recipes For Living Well

Raymond M. Binkowski

DISCLAIMER

Raymond M. Binkowski is not a physician or registered dietitian. The contents of this book should not be taken as medical advice. The book is not intended to diagnose, treat, cure or prevent any health problem – nor is it intended to replace the advice of a physician. Always consult your physician or qualified health professional on any matters regarding your health.

Print: ISBN-13: 978-0-9970048-9-2
ePUB: ISBN-13: 978-0-9848286-7-8
MOBI: ISBN-13: 978-0-9848286-8-5

Eatbycolor.com * #EatbyColor * @EatbyColor * facebook.com/EatbyColor

Interior design by booknook.biz

The Extra gets the Extra, Always! – Raymond M. Binkowski

Sophie and Vince always do the extra!

Special thanks to my family for eating these foods and allowing me to interrupt our meals to take food pictures. "Don't eat yet! I need to take pictures!"

Special thanks to Dr. Caughron for reviewing, editing, editing again and again. Danielle for the table of content formatting suggestions. David Olson, thanks for the creative direction.

To my staff and members for looking at countless iterations of cover art and food pictures.

Other Books

by Raymond M. Binkowski

All three available in print and your favorite digital format!

Interested in another week's menu of meals?

EatbyColor.com/menu

Connect with us on Social Media!

Facebook.com/EatbyColor

Instagram.com/EatbyColor

Twitter.com/EatbyColor

Pinterest.com/EatbyColor

https://www.amazon.com/Raymond-M.-Binkowski/e/B006MUG4TI/ref=sr_ntt_srch_
lnk_1?qid=1544014821&sr=8-1

Youtube.com/FitWorkzDeKalb

Contents

Not Just Another Recipe Book

THIS IS NOT JUST ANOTHER recipe book. It is not a diet book either. Most recipe books are loaded with recipes that have many ingredients. Unfortunately, many of the recipes call for ingredients that you do not have in your kitchen or any place else in your house. These books often are not geared toward weight loss and long-term maintenance. The books that are geared toward weight-loss suggest removing entire food groups, food or provide some other short-term approach (in other words diet) that can not be followed long-term.

So what is this book?

First, it is going to teach you how to eat. Eat by Color and Macro are two different approaches to eating provided to teach you how much to eat of what types of foods. Second, there are over 150 recipes that are easy to make with only a handful of ingredients. Third, there is a one-week, done-for-you menu plan so you can start eating better immediately.

Must Have In Your Kitchen

I REMEMBER BUYING MY FIRST weight-loss cookbook. I was excited to get it home only to find out there were two problems. First, I did not have the majority of the ingredients for any of the recipes in the book. Second, as a bachelor I did not have most of the utensils or kitchen equipment needed to make the food in the book. The new weight-loss book was loaded with food and meals I lacked the tools and ingredients to make. Your kitchen needs to have the tools for you to make the right foods to reach your goals. Recipes need to have only a few common ingredients or you are never going to make them OR will only make them on special occasions. This book is full of simple recipes with a handful of ingredients that you can easily make at home.

Here is a list of things you will need to have in your kitchen to put the recipes in this book to work for you.

Equipment and Tools

- Oven/Stove
- Microwave
- Grill
- Large Frying Pan with Lid
- Spatula
- Oven and Microwave Safe Dishware
- Pack of Portable Plastic Food Storage Containers (hit your local box store)
- Crock Pot or Slow Cooker
- Blender

Ingredients

- Garlic Powder
- Oregano
- Thyme
- Basil
- Olive Oil
- Balsamic Vinegar
- Salt and Pepper
- Vegetable Oil
- Butter
- Non-Stick Cooking Spray
- Mayonnaise
- Ranch Dressing
- Ranch Dressing Mix Packet
- Taco Seasoning
- Salsa
- Hot Sauce
- Vanilla Extract
- Mint Extract
- Honey
- Pumpkin Spice
- Allspice
- Nutmeg

The Secret to Eating to Reach Your Goals is NOT Another Diet

ANY APPROACH TO NUTRITION CAN work. The secret, if there is one is this: can you do it the rest of your life? Unfortunately, it is all too common that you can't. How many times have you heard of a new diet, tried it and made some great progress only to find you cannot stick with the new diet? The pounds and inches disappear only to return. The goal is not to lose pounds and inches only to gain them back later. The secret test is as simple as asking yourself "Can I do this forever?" If the answer is "No," the approach to nutrition will fail.

The second part of the secret is that the law of conservation of energy states energy cannot be created nor destroyed. Applied to calories, if you eat more calories than you spend, they have to go someplace (fat); if you eat fewer calories than you need, they have to come from someplace (fat.) To lose weight you have to spend more energy than you consume. To gain weight, consume more calories than you spend.

There are two long-term approaches that we have seen work well, notice LONG term! In each approach, calories are managed. The first approach is *Eat by Color*. The second manages calories by hitting targets. Both approaches provide simple ways to manage the calories you eat. Neither approach eliminates entire food groups, which most people cannot do long-term.

If you live a busy life, consider a food preparation service. There are many food services that will provide meals for the week. You can choose from a menu of meals that fit your nutrition goals. This will save on the shopping, preparation and cooking. For those that do not have time, this is a wise investment.

Eat by Color:
How to Eat Successfully without Dieting

Eat by Color teaches people a simple, long-term way to make better food choices: food choices that would facilitate weight loss, long-term weight management, and overall health and wellness. In *Eat by Color* the food groups are color coded. Protein is blue, carbohydrates are red, fats are purple and grow-in-your-back-yard-garden vegetables are green. Like children's paint-by-number paintings, meals are created by combining foods from the color-coded groups in the manner below. The approach is long-term, so the weight you lose, you lose forever.

Eat a Fist-Size Serving of Protein at Every Meal

Eat Carbs 2-4 Times per Day

Eat One Piece of Fruit per Day, Counts for One of the 2-4 Carbs Above

Eat 30 Grams of Fiber per Day[1]

Eat 20-30 Grams of Healthy Fat per Day

Eat all the Vegetables you want as OFTEN as you can

Drink One to Two Gallons of Water per Day

NEVER ALLOW YOURSELF TO GO HUNGRY

If you really want something, HAVE IT. Life is TOO SHORT

---

1. Google it! Want to know sources of fiber, Google fiber and pick food sources you like!

Protein	Vegetables*
If it was walking, flying or swimming, it is protein.	If you can grow it in your garden, it is probably going to fall into this group.
Cottage Cheese	Asparagus
Yogurt	Broccoli
String Cheese	Lettuce
Veggie (Meatless Patties)	Green Beans
Soy	Radishes
Chicken	Green Peppers, Red Peppers, Yellow Peppers, Orange Peppers
Lean Beef	Hot Peppers
Turkey	Spinach
Fish	Tomatoes
Protein Powder	Onions
Eggs	Mushrooms
	Cauliflower
	Celery
	Cucumbers
	Carrots

*You can eat as many or as much of these as you like! They can even be added to meals that do not include them!

Fruits	
○ Apples, any variety, Granny Smith are best	○ Papaya
	○ Peaches
○ Bananas	○ Plums
○ Pineapple	○ Raspberries
○ Cantaloupe	○ Blueberries
○ Cherries	○ Blackberries
○ Grapefruit	○ Strawberries
○ Grapes	○ Mangos
○ Honeydew Melon	○ Watermelon
○ Nectarines	○ Pears
○ Oranges	

Carbohydrates

- What we traditionally call starches or complex carbs.
- Rice, white or brown
- Potatoes, sweet, white, red, etc.
- Yams
- Winter Squash
- Pumpkin
- Oatmeal
- Cous Cous
- True Whole Grain Breads
- Peas
- Corn
- Beans and Legumes of all types

Fats

Olive Oil	Almonds
Flax Seed Oil	Pecans
Fish Oil, EPA/DHA	Cashews
Sunflower Oil	Butter
Safflower Oil	Heavy Whipping Cream
Walnuts	Flax Meal or Flax Seeds

Free Foods

- These foods you can eat all you want of.
- Spices
- Sugar Substitutes: Equal, Splenda, Stevia, Sweet n Low
- Vinegar
- Sugar-Free Gum
- Unsweetened Coffee and Tea
- Diet Beverages

Meal 1

2 Scoops Protein

Handful of Berries of any type

1 TBS Heavy Whipping Cream

Meal 1

Fist-Size Protein

Fist-Size Fruit

Serving of Healthy Fat

Meal 2 or Meal 4

2 Eggs and 3 Egg Whites

Salsa

Meal 2 or Meal 4

Fist-Size Protein

Fist-Size Insulin Impacting Carb

Meal 3

Fist-Size Chicken Breast, Lean Meat or Fish

Large salad with mixed vegetables

Vinegar and 1 TBS Oil

Meal 3

Fist-Size Protein

Unlimited Vegetables

Serving of Healthy Fat

Meal 2 or Meal 4

2 Scoops Protein

Handful of Berries of any type

1 TBS Heavy Whipping Cream

Meal 2 or Meal 4

Fist-Size Protein

Fist-Size Fruit

Serving of Healthy Fat

Meal 2 or Meal 4

2 Pieces of String Cheese

Piece of Fruit

Meal 2 or Meal 4

Fist-Size Protein

Fist-Size Fruit

Meal 2 or Meal 4

Jerky

Piece of Fruit

Meal 2 or Meal 4

Fist-Size Protein

Fist-Size Fruit

Meal 2 or Meal 4

1 Single Serving Low Carb Greek Yogurt

Handful of Mixed Nuts

Meal 2 or Meal 4

Fist-Size Protein

Serving of Healthy Fat

Meal 5

Fist Size Chicken Breast, Lean Meat or Fish

Salad

1 TBS vinegar, Balsamic is fine

1 TBS of olive oil as dressing

Meal 5

Fist-Size Protein

Unlimited Vegetables

1 TBS vinegar, Balsamic is fine!

Serving of Healthy Fat

A Guide to Calories, Macros, Flexible Dieting and IIFYM (If It Fits Your Macros)

ANOTHER APPROACH TO NUTRITION IS to track calories, carbohydrates, protein and fat. Rather than looking at the numbers as limits, it is best to see them as targets. Calories are a measure of energy. Remember, to lose weight, more calories have to be spent than consumed. Calories, carbohydrates, protein and fat are macronutrients and are often referred to as macros. A number of names and acronyms have been applied to this approach, yet they are the same.

Tracking calories, carbohydrates, protein and fat has been made easy thanks to technology. There are great applications on your favorite mobile device that make tracking easy. Many are even free of charge. The *My Fitness Pal* application is one of the most popular at the time this is being written and is the one many of our clients use. It does not matter how you track and measure your progress to your goals, what matters is that you are consistently hitting the goals.

Calories
How many should you eat? Ten times your current bodyweight in calories is a great place to start.

Protein
- One gram per pound of bodyweight
- Protein contains four calories per gram

Carbohydrates
- 20-30% of Calories
- Carbohydrates contain four calories per gram

Fat
- The Balance of Calories remaining
- Fat contains nine calories per gram
- For example, let's say we have a 150-pound individual
- Total Calories per Day
- 10 X 150 = 1500 calories

Guide to Calculate Protein
- 150 grams
- 150 X 4 = 600 Calories

Guide to Calculate Carbohydrates
- 30% of 1500
- .30 X 1500 = 450 calories from carbohydrates
- 450 / 4 = 112.5 grams of carbohydrates

Guide to Calculate Fat
- 1500 – 1050 = 450 calories from fat
- 450 / 9 = 50 grams of fat
- So for the 150 pound person in the above example

Nutrition Targets
- 1500
- Protein
- 150 grams
- Carbohydrates
- 112.5 grams
- Fat
- 50 grams

These numbers become your targets and get entered into *My Fitness Pal* or similar tracking application. Your goal is to hit these targets everyday.

Turning Diet Myths into Nutrition Truths

As a trainer, gym owner and author I have spent the last two decades working with thousands of people on nutrition, training and lifestyle. The following are the most common myths and misconceptions clients have had.

You have to eat 6 small meals per day.
There is no truth to this. We have had successful clients eating 3 meals per day. Work and life commitments make it impossible to eat this often. If you can only eat 4 times per day you are not dead in the water. Make better food choices for those 4 meals and move on.

You can't eat carbs. (Applies to the Atkins and younger generation of Keto folks)
Most people are overeating carbs and not getting enough protein. Increasing protein and cutting back on carbs are often steps in the right direction. Eliminating carbs completely is not necessary and cannot be done indefinitely. When it comes to nutrition, your success is in a long-term approach. Completely eliminating carbs for the rest of your life is not going to happen.

Cheat Days, Cheat Meals and Dieting Always.
If you really want something, have it. You do not need a day of the week or meal of the week to do it. What if a special event (wedding/anniversary/graduation/birthday) happens on a Wednesday but your cheat day is Saturday? Are you really going to miss the special event because it falls on the wrong day of the week? This makes no sense and again is not likely to work long-term.

If you have six days a week of better food choices, one day a week, regardless of which day of the week, is not going to stop progress. On a monthly basis this will be

25-28 good days of eating and on an annual basis over 300 days of good eating. Three hundred days of good eating are enough to make progress and reach your goals.

Always being strict with food and dieting means life will pass you by. Friends, family and loved ones will not be here forever. Enjoy those special events. Don't let life pass you by.

Alcohol/Beer/Wine

If you want it have it, just not all the time. If you are making progress and have the occasional drink, it will not matter. If you are not making progress, then the drink might have to be eliminated. Should you drink vodka because you heard it has the lowest carbs or calories? If that is what you want to drink, then yes. You are better off just having what you enjoy. Just do not go overboard.

Eating after 6:00 PM, 7:00 PM or Later

It does not matter what time the calories come in. What matters is that calories are not consumed in excess of calories burned. Plenty of our clients eat before bed and have no issues losing pounds and inches. The bigger picture is making sure you eat enough calories, but not too many.

Detoxes and Cleanses

Contrary to what the multi-level marketing people say on the Internet, a detox and/or a cleanse is not necessary for weight loss and long-term weight maintenance. Plenty have lost pounds and inches and kept them off long-term without doing either.

Forever Cutting Calories

Initially cutting calories gets the scale moving down. There is a point where cutting calories will not keep the scale moving down and a plateau will happen. In some cases, if calories go too low, the scale might actually go up. Cutting calories is not always the answer and we see people make great progress by actually increasing their calories. Read that again. Many people that lose weight and keep it off for the long-term actually have to eat MORE not less!

Eat Right for Even the Busiest Lifestyle

LONG-TERM HEALTH, WELLNESS AND WEIGHT loss require a simple and convenient approach to food. Here are some tips that make eating better easy.

1. If pressed for time, pick up a rotisserie chicken.
2. Get creative with leftovers.
3. Meal-plan and shop on one day.
4. Prepare meals for at least the workweek and workday.
5. Buy a set of individual meal containers and a cooler bag.
6. Keep a shaker bottle in your car, office or workspace.
7. Put two scoops of protein in a bag and keep in your shaker bottle above.
8. If you must hit the drivethrough, decide right now a grilled chicken salad and low-fat or light dressing is what you are ordering.
9. String cheese, mixed nuts, peanuts and protein bars can be found at almost every gas station today and make great snack options when you are filling up.
10. Pre-make and place in freezer bags meals you make in your crock pot.
11. Master cooking the Basics in the Kitchen

    a. How to cook chicken breast
    b. How to make and cook burgers
    c. How to make tacos
    d. How to cook a steak
    e. How to cook eggs

Easy 7-Day Menu and Meal Plan

THE GREAT-TASTING RECIPES IN THIS book are easy to make. Planning for the week ahead makes life easy. A sample 7-day menu plan can be found at the end of this section.

First you need the plan or the menu for the week. Second, the groceries. If you shop on one day, and cook and meal-prep on the next day, things are easy.

On Saturday create a grocery list and grocery shop. On Sunday prep and get ready for the week. This will make following the meal plan during the week possible. If you do not put in the time to plan, you will struggle during the week. If the struggle is great enough you are likely to hit the drivethrough window and order junk. Reduce the struggle by planning and preparing.

Meals in the menu are labeled Meal 1, Meal 2 and so on. You can have breakfast for lunch or dinner for breakfast. Make eating convenient for you, your lifestyle and your likes. The order of the meals really does not matter. Switch them around. Eat them when it is convenient to do so. It is better to eat the right meals whenever that may be than to make the wrong food choices at the right time.

You have to manage the calories you consume relative to the calories you burn. This means eating the right portions of the foods in the meals below relative to your goals. Follow *Eat by Color* and the macro/calorie counting method mentioned previously to portion the meals that follow to fit your goals.

Below is a week's menu of meals.

Day 1

Meal 1	On-the-Go Baked Eggs
Meal 2	Triple Chocolate Delight
Meal 3	Tuna Wrap
Meal 4	Homemade Burgers
	Mashed Cauliflower

Day 2

Meal 1	Eggs and English Muffin
Meal 2	Peanut Butter Cup
Meal 3	Naked Burger and Vegetables
Meal 4	Crust-Free Pizza
Meal 5	Grilled Chicken and Vegetables

Day 3

Meal 1	Healthy Protein Waffles
Meal 2	Chocolate Thinner Mint
Meal 3	Chicken Lettuce Wrap
Meal 4	High-Protein Ranch Dip
Meal 5	Chicken Sweet Pepper Pizza

Day 4

Meal 1	Key Lime Protein Pie
Meal 2	Chocolate Covered Strawberries
Meal 3	Low Carb Rice Free Asian Chicken
Meal 4	Celery and Peanut Butter
Meal 5	Cilantro Lime Crock Pot Chicken

Day 5

Meal 1	Portable Egg Muffin
Meal 2	White Chocolate Protein Shake
Meal 3	Cilantro Lime Crock Pot Chicken
Meal 4	On-the-Go Baked Eggs
Meal 5	Cilantro Lime Chicken Quesadilla
Meal 6	Yogurt Protein Parfait

Day 6

Meal 1	Overnight Oats N Protein
Meal 2	Key Lime Pie
Meal 3	Leftover Chicken Wrap
Meal 4	Dine Out
Meal 5	Caprese Tomato Mozzarella

Day 7

Meal 1	Egg Bake
Meal 2	French Vanilla Shake
Meal 3	Healthy Drivethrough
Meal 4	Pumpkin Pie Protein Pudding
Meal 5	Zesty Lime Shrimp and Avocado Salad

How to Reduce Calories, Carbs or Fat

TOTAL CALORIES CONSUMED ON A daily, weekly and monthly basis matter. Learn to read nutrition labels on food. Better yet, get an app that will allow you to scan bar codes on food then display the calories, carbs, fat and protein. The better your knowledge of the foods you eat, the easier you will find it to manage your food. There is no way to skip out on this self-education. You have to develop a basic knowledge of what you are eating for yourself.

Reducing Calories

Once you understand what you are eating, it is easy to lower calories. Simply reducing portion sizes is a great start to lowering calories. Cutting the extras, like condiments, helps. Take the butter out. Many recipes and foods call for butter, but the butter may not be needed (I remember asking my mom why there was butter in a particular meal and her answer was that is the way Grandma made it).

Reducing Carbs

Foods may be labeled reduced sugar, low sugar and sugar free. Look for sugar free or reduced sugar. Sugar free and reduced sugar will be reduced carb or no carb. Learn what foods you can reduce or remove carbs from.

Reducing Fat

Dietary fat is not the enemy of fat loss. Fat plays a role in everything from feeling full after a meal to the production of hormones. So do not completely eliminate fat. If you are taking a calorie and macro approach to eating, you may find that eating animal proteins makes it hard to hit your fat and protein targets without going over on either. If so, you may want to reduce fat in other areas of your meal or meals. Reduced fat, low fat and fat-free are the words you should look for on packaging. There are many foods and recipes that have fat but do not need it. Use non-stick cooking spray in place of butter or oil. Learn what foods you can reduce or remove the fat from and it will make it easier to hit your fat target but not go over.

Using spices and seasonings is a great way to take calories, carbs and fat out of meals without compromising on taste. Carbs and fat make food taste good. Often if they are removed, food suddenly does not taste so good. Adding seasoning and spices might make a food or meal taste better.

Making your own dressings and sauces puts you in control of what goes into them. You can make great vinaigrettes that are low-calorie, fat-free and sugar-free. Just keep in mind that you do not want to completely eliminate fat from your diet. Also, that "fat-free" typically means more carbohydrates.

Understanding Nutrition Facts

ALMOST EVERY FOOD AND DRINK will be labeled with nutrition facts. The first thing to look for is information about servings. Some products will appear low in calories until you realize what the intended serving size is and how many servings are in the container. Make sure you read and understand the serving size. For example many 16-20 fluid-ounce drinks have 2-2.5 servings in them. The label may say 100 calories per serving but if you drink the entire bottle or can it is really 200-250 calories.

If you are using an application on your mobile device or a website on your computer to look up calories and macros, pay attention to what you enter and look up. Make sure to enter the correct amount of the food or drink. Also be aware of the brand and type you are entering. Entering the incorrect amount or wrong brand can provide calorie and macro amounts that are wrong.

The recipes that follow have a nutrition fact table. These are approximations! Different brands and different sources of information can produce different numbers from those here. Be sure to look up the information for the specific brands you use.

Breakfast

Portable Egg Muffin

BELIEVE IT OR NOT, THE recipe for the egg muffin above took minutes to make. In this case not only is the egg muffin convenient but it is portable and nutritious.

Ingredients:
- 2 Eggs
- 1 English Muffin
- 2 ounces of Shredded Cheddar Cheese (if you are so inclined)
- Black Pepper

Scramble the eggs. Toast your English muffin. Once the eggs are cooked, place between the muffin halves, top with your favorite cheese. Boom, wow, done…portable egg muffin in minutes!

Portable Egg Muffin	
Servings	1
	Per Serving
Calories	326
Fat g	19
Saturated Fat g	2
Cholesterol mg	636
Carbohydrates g	25
Fiber g	3
Sugar g	0
Protein g	33
Sodium	368

Coconut Protein Pancakes

HIGH-PROTEIN AND HIGH-TASTE BREAKFAST OPTIONS are possible. Even the kids will like this one.

Ingredients:
- 2 scoops Vanilla Protein Powder
- ¼ cup Coconut Flour
- ½ cup Coconut Milk
- 4 Egg Whites
- 1 Tsp. Vanilla Extract
- 1 Tsp. Honey

Combine all ingredients in a mixing bowl. Whip and mix with a fork or whisk. You want a thick pancake batter consistency. Heat frying pan or griddle and cook just like you would any pancake. Enjoy!

Coconut Protein Pancakes	
Servings	2
	Per Serving
Calories	243
Fat g	12
Saturated Fat g	2
Cholesterol mg	315
Carbohydrates g	16
Fiber g	5
Sugar g	7
Protein g	35
Sodium mg	271

Healthy Protein Waffles

KIDS LOVE THESE AND SO will you. Healthy, protein waffles you can make at home. Why buy them at the store? Store-bought are high in carbs, sugar, preservatives and price. Why not teach your kids about healthy eating and get them involved in the kitchen? Get the kids involved. Have them help out in the kitchen.

Ingredients:
- 8 Scoops Vanilla Protein Powder
- 1 Box Pancake Mix
- 4 Cups Water
- 2/3 Cup Vegetable Oil
- 2 Eggs

Add all ingredients to large mixing bowl. Mix with a wire whisk or use a hand mixer. You want a thick batter. If too thick, add water and if too thin, add more protein powder. Turn on waffle iron and follow instructions for waffle iron. This will make 25-30 waffles depending on size of waffle iron. Freeze leftovers for later. Batter can also be used to make pancakes.

Healthy Protein Waffles	
Servings	20
	Per Serving
Calories	186
Fat g	7
Saturated Fat g	1
Cholesterol mg	14
Carbohydrates g	21
Fiber g	1
Sugar g	2
Protein g	14
Sodium	439

Pumpkin Protein Waffles

Ingredients:
- 8 Scoops Vanilla Protein Powder
- 1 Box Pancake Mix
- 1 Can Pure Pumpkin (do not get the can of pumpkin pie filling)
- 4 Cups Water
- 2/3 Cup Vegetable Oil
- ½ Scoop Vanilla Protein
- 1 Tsp. Pumpkin Spice

Add all ingredients to large mixing bowl. Mix with a wire whisk or use a hand mixer. You want a thick batter. If too thick, add water and if too thin, add more protein powder. Turn on waffle iron and follow instructions for waffle iron. This will make 25-30 waffles depending on size of waffle iron. Freeze leftovers for later. Batter can also be used to make pancakes.

Pumpkin Protein Waffles	
Servings	20
	Per Serving
Calories	290
Fat g	11
Saturated Fat g	1
Cholesterol mg	22
Carbohydrates g	34
Fiber g	2
Sugar g	4
Protein g	22
Sodium	660

As a topping, mix a half-scoop of vanilla protein with 1 Tsp. of pumpkin spice. Add 2 TBS water and mix with a whisk. This makes a pumpkin spice frosting of sorts.

Protein Waffle Dipping Sticks

REMOVE ALREADY-MADE PROTEIN WAFFLE (PUMPKIN Protein Waffles pictured) from freezer. Microwave for 30-60 seconds. Drop in toaster and cut into sticks. Dip in your favorite syrup. Kids love these!

Protein Waffle Dipping Sticks	
Servings	20
	Per Serving
Calories	290
Fat g	11
Saturated Fat g	1
Cholesterol mg	22
Carbohydrates g	34
Fiber g	2
Sugar g	4
Protein g	22
Sodium	660

Eggs and English Muffins

Ingredients:

- 3 Eggs
- 1 English Muffin
- Butter
- Salt and Pepper

Heat non-stick frying pan or cast iron skillet. Coat pan with butter or use your favorite non-stick spray. Break eggs and cook sunny side up. Split English muffin and place in toaster. Eggs will cook in minutes and the muffin in less time. If you do not want your yolks runny, cook longer.

Eggs and English Muffins	
Servings	1
	Per Serving
Calories	340
Fat g	22
Saturated Fat g	0
Cholesterol mg	930
Carbohydrates g	25
Fiber g	3
Sugar g	0
Protein g	37
Sodium	420

Scrambled Egg Wrap

Ingredients:
- 2 Eggs
- 1 High-Fiber Wrap
- 2 TBS Shredded Cheddar Cheese
- 2 TBS Salsa

Make those scrambled eggs portable using a high-fiber wrap. Scramble a few eggs (keep the yolks or don't, up to you.) Try adding these extras to your wrap: cheese, salsa, sausage, bacon, peppers, hot sauce and more! Repurpose leftovers from yesterday's dinner in the wrap. Great way to repurpose leftovers!

Scrambled Egg Wrap	
Servings	1
	Per Serving
Calories	306
Fat g	20
Saturated Fat g	2
Cholesterol mg	636
Carbohydrates g	23
Fiber g	7
Sugar g	4
Protein g	36
Sodium mg	808

Egg, Vegetable, Chicken and Sausage Wrap

Ingredients:

- ½ Cup Vegetables (leftover broccoli, carrots and cauliflower - basically a California blend)
- 4 Ounces Grilled Chicken (leftover)
- 1 High-Fiber Wrap
- 2 Eggs
- 1 TBS Olive Oil
- 2 Ounces Shredded Cheese

Toss everything except the wrap into a frying pan with some olive oil. Everything has already been cooked so just warm everything up in the pan. In a second frying pan scramble some eggs. You can use one whole egg or just two to three egg whites to reduce calories and fat. Add to a wrap. Top with salsa, hot sauce or whatever floats your boat.

Egg, Vegetable, Chicken and Sausage Wrap	
Servings	1
	Per Serving
Calories	550
Fat g	34
Saturated Fat g	3
Cholesterol mg	740
Carbohydrates g	26
Fiber g	9
Sugar g	4
Protein g	66
Sodium mg	980

Peanut Butter Waffle Sandwich

Ingredients:
- Protein Waffles
- Peanut Butter

Check out the protein waffle recipe in this book. If you meal-prep and make batches of waffles in advance they can be frozen. Simply pull a waffle or two out of the freezer, drop in the toaster and when they are done, cut in half, add peanut butter and make into a waffle sandwich. Kids love them. They are portable and taste great.

Peanut Butter Waffle Sandwich	
Servings	1
	Per Serving
Calories	376
Fat g	23
Saturated Fat g	3
Cholesterol mg	14
Carbohydrates g	29
Fiber g	3
Sugar g	5
Protein g	21
Sodium mg	579

Egg White Pancakes

Ingredients:

- 2 Eggs
- 6 Egg Whites
- 1 Cup Rolled Oats, dry
- 1 Cup Cottage Cheese
- 2 Tsp. Sugar
- 1 Tsp. Cinnamon
- 1 Tsp. Vanilla Extract

Blend all ingredients until smooth in a blender. Heat a large non-stick skillet over medium-low heat. Spray with non-stick cooking spray. For each pancake pour 1/4 cup of batter onto skillet. Flip when they start to bubble. Cook until golden-brown. Repeat with remaining batches, spraying the skillet as needed. Makes about 8 pancakes. Leftovers can be frozen for later.

Egg White Pancakes	
Servings	8
	Per Serving
Calories	99
Fat g	3
Saturated Fat g	1
Cholesterol mg	81
Carbohydrates g	11
Fiber g	2
Sugar g	1
Protein g	9
Sodium mg	178

Wahoo (Fish) Egg Bake

Ingredients:
- 5 Eggs
- 1 Cup Shredded Cheese
- 1/2 Vidalia Onion
- 1 TBS Butter
- 8 Ounces Sweet Potato
- 8 Ounces Grilled Wahoo (Any leftover white fish will do)

Preheat oven to 350-400F. The ever-popular disclaimer...cooking times and temps will differ with oven. Dice the onion. Coat frying pan with 1 TBS of butter and melt on low heat. Brown onion in the pan. While you are doing this, bake a small or medium sweet potato in the microwave for 4-6 minutes. Slice the baked sweet potato into thin slices. Once the onions are browned, remove the onion from the frying pan.

Recoat the frying pan with butter. Place fish in bottom of the pan. Place the sliced sweet potato and layer the slices on each other until they cover the bottom of the pan. Top with onions and cheese. Whip/beat the eggs in a bowl and pour over everything in the pan. Bake for 20-25 minutes. Makes about eight servings. Top with salsa or hot sauce and enjoy.

Wahoo (Fish) Egg Bake	
Servings	8
	Per Serving
Calories	215
Fat g	16
Saturated Fat g	3
Cholesterol mg	420
Carbohydrates g	7
Fiber g	1
Sugar g	1
Protein g	23
Sodium mg	291

High-Protein Egg Bake

Ingredients:
- 5 Eggs
- 1 Cup Shredded Cheese
- 1/2 Vidalia Onion
- 1 TBS Butter
- 8 Ounces Sweet Potato
- High-Fiber Tortillas

Preheat oven to 350-400F. The ever popular disclaimer…cooking times and temps will differ with oven. Chop, slice and dice onion. Coat frying pan with 1 TBS butter on low heat. Brown onion. While you are doing this, bake a small or medium sweet potato in the microwave for 4-6 minutes. Slice the baked sweet potato into thin slices. Once the onions are browned, remove the onion from the frying pan.

Recoat the frying pan with butter. Place sliced sweet potato in pan covering the bottom, layering the slices on each other until they are all in the pan. Top with onions and cheese. Whip/beat the eggs in a bowl and pour over everything in the pan. Bake for 20-25 minutes. Serves eight. Top with hot sauce or salsa.

High-Protein Egg Bake	
Servings	8
	Per Serving
Calories	239
Fat g	16
Saturated Fat g	3
Cholesterol mg	402
Carbohydrates g	23
Fiber g	9
Sugar g	1
Protein g	22
Sodium mg	538

Ingredients:

- 13 Eggs
- 1 Sweet Red Pepper
- 1/2 Vidalia Onion
- 1 TBS Butter
- 8 Ounces Sweet Potato
- 6 Ounces Fingerling Potatoes
- 1 Cup Cheddar Cheese

Egg bakes are a great way to make breakfast for a few days at one time. Great to do on Saturday or Sunday morning.

Break eggs into a mixing bowl. Whip or mix the eggs...same thing you would do if making scrambled eggs. Wash, core and remove seeds, slice and dice the pepper. Dice the onion. Sauté pepper and onion in 1 TBS of butter. Wash all potatoes, then microwave for 4-6 minutes. Slice potatoes in thin strips. Coat oven safe baking dish or cast-iron frying pan. Layer the potato slices on the bottom of the pan. Place onions and peppers on top of the potatoes. Pour eggs on top. Top with cheese. Bake at 350F for 25-35 minutes.

Double Potato Egg Bake	
Servings	8
	Per Serving
Calories	274
Fat g	22
Saturated Fat g	2
Cholesterol mg	790
Carbohydrates g	11
Fiber g	2
Sugar g	4
Protein g	35
Sodium mg	446

High-Protein French Toast

Ingredients:

- 1 Whole Egg
- 1 Scoop Strawberry Protein Powder
- 3/4 Cup Almond Milk
- 2 Pieces of High-Fiber Bread
- 1 TBS Butter
- Light/Low-Cal/ or Zero-Cal Syrup

Mix egg, protein powder and almond milk in a bowl or blender bottle. Pour mix in a bowl and dip the bread in it. Be sure to coat both sides. Put butter in a frying pan or use non-stick cooking spray. Cook the bread slices. They are done when they are starting to get crispy. Top with fresh fruit or low-calorie syrup of your choice and liking.

High-Protein French Toast	
Servings	1
	Per Serving
Calories	412
Fat g	27
Saturated Fat g	7
Cholesterol mg	346
Carbohydrates g	30
Fiber g	6.5
Sugar g	5.5
Protein g	39
Sodium mg	732

Sliced Roast Beef and Egg Muffin

Ingredients:
- 1/2 Pound Roast Beef (Leftovers work great)
- 6 Eggs
- 4 Whole Grain English Muffins
- 2 TBS Cheddar Cheese
- 1 TBS Butter

Slice leftover beef as thin as possible. Place in frying pan and warm up on low heat. Remember the beef is already cooked so we are just reheating it. Scramble the eggs. Toast the English muffins. Butter the muffins. Place beef on muffin halves and top with cheese and eggs.

Sliced Roast Beef and Egg Muffin	
Servings	4
	Per Serving
Calories	394
Fat g	16
Saturated Fat g	6
Cholesterol mg	54
Carbohydrates g	29
Fiber g	2
Sugar g	2
Protein g	47
Sodium mg	222

Gourmet Egg Sandwich

PORTABLE BREAKFAST EGG MUFFIN SANDWICH will make having breakfast on the way out the door easy!

Ingredients:
- 4 Eggs
- 2 Whole Grain English Muffins
- 2 Ounces Havarti cheese
- 1 TBS Butter (Yes, butter – it really is not bad for you)

Cook the eggs… put a lid on the frying pan so the eggs cook faster. Split and toast the muffin. When the eggs are done, put them on two of the muffin halves, top with Havarti cheese and make a sandwich with the other muffin halves. Step out of your comfort zone and try some different cheeses like the Havarti in this recipe.

Gourmet Egg Sandwich	
Servings	2
	Per Serving
Calories	561
Fat g	20
Saturated Fat g	10
Cholesterol mg	60
Carbohydrates g	37
Fiber g	3
Sugar g	3
Protein g	94
Sodium mg	721

On-the-Go Baked Eggs

Ingredients:
- ○ 1 Dozen Eggs
- ○ Fresh Spinach
- ○ Tomato
- ○ Non Stick Cooking Spray

Preheat your oven to 350F. Coat a cupcake tin with non-stick cooking spray. Break one egg into each cupcake cup. Add vegetables or your favorite ingredients. Place tin in oven and bake for 20-30 minutes, again depending on oven. Eggs can be refrigerated for future meals and go great on English muffins!

On-the-Go Baked Eggs	
Servings	6
	Per Serving
Calories	280
Fat g	4
Saturated Fat g	0
Cholesterol mg	20
Carbohydrates g	12
Fiber g	2
Sugar g	2
Protein g	84
Sodium mg	90

Baked Hard Boiled Eggs

Ingredients:
- ○ 1 Dozen Eggs

Baked hard-boiled eggs. How can an egg be baked and hard-boiled? Great question. Let's take a step back. Eggs are an affordable source of protein. Hard-boiled eggs are also portable. Portable protein sources make life convenient. There are three problems with boiling eggs. First, a large pot of boiling water on top of the stove is a concern if you have small children. Second, having to watch the pot for boil over. Third, having to peel the shells that sometimes just do not want to come off the egg. Baking the eggs provides all of the convenience of a hard-boiled egg without the three concerns listed above. Preheat your oven to 350F. Place the eggs into cupcake tin. Place tin in the oven and bake for 20-30 minutes depending on oven.

Baked Hard Boiled Eggs	
Servings	6
	Per Serving
Calories	280
Fat g	4
Saturated Fat g	0
Cholesterol mg	20
Carbohydrates g	12
Fiber g	2
Sugar g	2
Protein g	84
Sodium mg	90

Overnight Oats N Protein

Ingredients:
- 2 Scoops Protein Powder
- 1/2 Cup Quick Oats
- Frozen Berries

Put 2 scoops of protein powder in a plastic bowl, add the oats and then water until you have a thick, almost paste consistency. Mix in some berries. DONE! Place in the fridge. Overnight the berries will melt and the oats will absorb the water.

Overnight Oats N Protein	
Servings	1
	Per Serving
Calories	425
Fat g	8
Saturated Fat g	1
Cholesterol mg	20
Carbohydrates g	43
Fiber g	5
Sugar g	7
Protein g	48
Sodium mg	400

Yogurt Protein Parfait

Ingredients:

- 1 Scoop Protein
- 1 Cup Low-Calorie Vanilla Greek Yogurt
- ½ Cup Handful Frozen Mixed Berries or Blueberries
- 1 TBS Flax Oil, Seed or Meal
- 4 Ounces Water

Mix all of the above. Easy way to start the day with protein, anti-oxidant and fiber-rich blueberries, healthy fat and fiber from the flax and the good bacteria from the Greek yogurt.

Yogurt Protein Parfait Servings	1
	Per Serving
Calories	345
Fat g	5
Saturated Fat g	1
Cholesterol mg	10
Carbohydrates g	35
Fiber g	12
Sugar g	14
Protein g	40
Sodium mg	200

Ingredients:
- 1 Can Tuna in Water
- 1 TBS Mayonnaise
- 1/4 Vidalia Onion
- 1 High-Fiber Wrap

Open the can of tuna and drain the water. Mix 1-2 TBS of Mayonnaise and salt (garlic salt or Mrs. Dash) to taste. Fill wrap then fold or roll.

Tuna Wrap	
Servings	1
	Per Serving
Calories	365
Fat g	16
Saturated Fat g	0
Cholesterol mg	63
Carbohydrates g	24
Fiber g	8
Sugar g	3
Protein g	41
Sodium mg	841

Fiesta Tuna Wrap

Ingredients:
- 1 Can Tuna in Water
- 2 TBS Salsa
- High-Fiber Wrap

Open the can of tuna and drain the water. Mix 1-2 TBS of salsa with the tuna. Fill wrap then fold or roll.

Fiesta Tuna Wrap	
Servings	1
	Per Serving
Calories	270
Fat g	5
Saturated Fat g	0
Cholesterol mg	63
Carbohydrates g	26
Fiber g	7
Sugar g	5
Protein g	41
Sodium mg	1230

Avocado Tuna Wrap

Ingredients:
- 1 Can Tuna in Water
- 1/2 Fresh Avocado
- High-Fiber Wrap

Open the can of tuna and drain the water. Slice or chop avocado. Combine avocado with tuna and add to wrap.

Avocado Tuna Wrap	
Servings	1
	Per Serving
Calories	367
Fat g	16
Saturated Fat g	2
Cholesterol mg	63
Carbohydrates g	26
Fiber g	12
Sugar g	4
Protein g	42
Sodium mg	935

Holy Guaca Tuna Wrap

Ingredients:
- 1 Can Tuna in Water
- 2 TBS Guacamole
- High-Fiber Wrap
- Salt (Lime Salt or Mrs. Dash)

Open the can of tuna and drain the water. Mix 1-2 TBS of guacamole and salt (lime salt or Mrs. Dash) to taste. Fill wrap then fold or roll.

Holy Guaca Tuna Wrap	
Servings	1
	Per Serving
Calories	341
Fat g	13
Saturated Fat g	1
Cholesterol mg	63
Carbohydrates g	25
Fiber g	11
Sugar g	3
Protein g	42
Sodium mg	726

Pollo Rancho Wrap

Ingredients:

- 12 Ounces Chicken Breasts (leftover grilled chicken works great)
- 4 TBS Light Ranch Dressing
- 2 High-Fiber Wraps
- 1 Cup Shredded Lettuce

Grill the chicken breasts. Slice or chop chicken. Mix with ranch dressing. Place in wrap, add lettuce and fold. Optional… toast the wrap to add some crunch.

Pollo Rancho Wrap	
Servings	2
	Per Serving
Calories	429
Fat g	16
Saturated Fat g	3
Cholesterol mg	146
Carbohydrates g	15
Fiber g	4
Sugar g	5
Protein g	57
Sodium mg	563

Italian Chicken Panini

Ingredients:
- 2 High-Fiber Wraps
- 12 Ounces Leftover Grilled or Baked Chicken Breast
- Mozzarella Cheese Shredded
- 1 Cup Spaghetti Sauce
- 1 TBS Butter

Slice or shred the chicken breast. Put 1 TBS of butter in a large skillet or frying pan. Once the butter has melted, add the wrap. Let the wrap heat then flip. Add shredded chicken. Now add sauce and cheese to your liking and in line with your goals. Fold the wrap in half. Flip wrap a few times so both sides are toasted and a bit crunchy. Top with some sauce and enjoy.

Italian Chicken Panini	
Servings	2
	Per Serving
Calories	576
Fat g	23
Saturated Fat g	10
Cholesterol mg	141
Carbohydrates g	25
Fiber g	7
Sugar g	12
Protein g	72
Sodium mg	1092

Leftover Chicken Wrap

Ingredients:
- 4 Ounce Shredded Chicken (leftover from crock pot meal)
- 1 Cup California Vegetables
- 1 TBS Olive Oil
- High-Fiber Wrap

Leftovers can get mundane, but they do not have to. Sometimes eating the same thing a few days in a row can lead to binging on something you really should not have. Keep it interesting. Here is one way to do that. Turn that leftover crock pot/slow cooker shredded chicken into an incredible wrap!

Combine chicken, veggies and oil in saucepan. Sauté. Then get your wrap and wrap it up. Done! Great-tasting low-carb wrap using leftovers in minutes! Top with some cheese, hot sauce or even guacamole (not included in nutrition info below).

Leftover Chicken Wrap	
Servings	1
	Per Serving
Calories	415
Fat g	20
Saturated Fat g	3
Cholesterol mg	0
Carbohydrates g	24
Fiber g	9
Sugar g	5
Protein g	43
Sodium mg	315

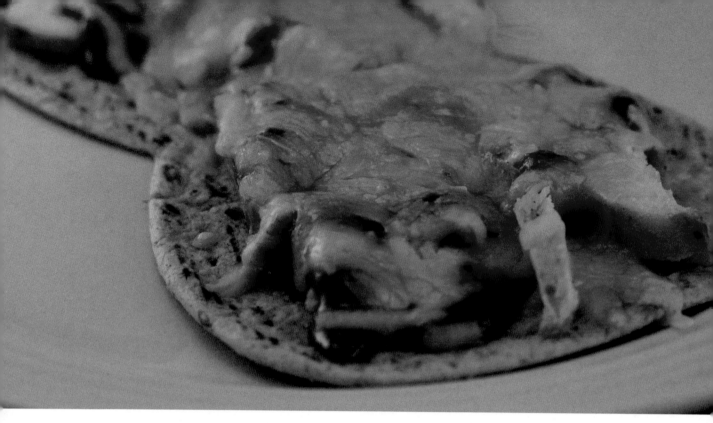

BBQ Chicken Flatbread Pizza

Ingredients:

- 8 Ounces Chicken Breast (leftovers)
- 6 TBS BBQ Sauce (get the low carb/sugar if you please)
- 1 Cup Shredded Cheddar
- 1 TBS Olive Oil
- 2 High-Fiber Wraps

BBQ Chicken Flatbread Pizza	
Servings	2
	Per Serving
Calories	484
Fat g	12
Saturated Fat g	7
Cholesterol mg	126
Carbohydrates g	35
Fiber g	4
Sugar g	20
Protein g	55
Sodium mg	845

Low carb. High protein. High fiber. Save time by using leftover chicken. Kids love them! What more can you ask for?

Put foil on a cookie sheet; this saves time at clean-up. Coat the foil with olive oil. Set oven to 350-375F. Slice the chicken thin. Place the chicken on the wrap. Spread some BBQ sauce. Top with cheddar. Bake for 12-15 minutes or until the wrap is crispy. Bonus: you can control the BBQ sauce, use low carb BBQ sauce and go easy on the cheddar... this will drop the calories, carbs and fat.

Chicken Lettuce Wrap

Ingredients:

- 8 Ounces Grilled Chicken Breast
- 4 TBS Salsa
- ½ Cup Lettuce
- 2 TBS Cheddar Cheese

Slice leftover grilled chicken. Place chicken on lettuce leaf with cheddar cheese and salsa. Wrap up and meal is done.

Chicken Lettuce Wrap	
Servings	2
	Per Serving
Calories	274
Fat g	7
Saturated Fat g	4
Cholesterol mg	111
Carbohydrates g	6
Fiber g	0
Sugar g	1
Protein g	39
Sodium mg	490

Chicken and Sweet Pepper Pizza Wrap

THERE ARE MANY VARIATIONS OF high-protein pizza using high-fiber wraps. Save time and repurpose leftovers in this recipe.

Ingredients:

- 2 High Fiber Wraps
- 12 Ounces Leftover Grilled or Baked Chicken Breast
- Mozzarella Cheese
- 1 Cup Spaghetti Sauce
- 1 Red Bell Pepper

Wash pepper, remove seeds, slice and sauté. Preheat oven to 320-350F. Place wraps on pizza stone or pizza pan. Top with leftover chicken, peppers (optional) and cheese. Cook for 10-15 minutes.

Chicken Sweet Pepper Pizza Wrap	
Servings	2
	Per Serving
Calories	601
Fat g	23
Saturated Fat g	10
Cholesterol mg	141
Carbohydrates g	27
Fiber g	8
Sugar g	14
Protein g	72
Sodium mg	1095

Cancun Chicken Wrap

Ingredients:
- 12 Ounces Grilled Chicken
- 4 TBS Guacamole (store-bought or make your own from the recipe in this book)
- 4 TBS Cheddar Cheese
- 4 TBS Salsa
- 2 High-Fiber Wraps

Slice chicken into strips. Top wraps with chicken and all of the other ingredients.

Cancun Chicken Wrap	
Servings	2
	Per Serving
Calories	470
Fat g	19
Saturated Fat g	6
Cholesterol mg	156
Carbohydrates g	17
Fiber g	6
Sugar g	3
Protein g	60
Sodium mg	566

A Healthier Taco Wrap

Ingredients:
- 2 Pounds 90% Lean Ground Beef
- Taco Seasoning Packets (or see taco seasoning recipe in this book)
- 1 Cup Cheddar Cheese
- 1 Cup Sour Cream (substitute plain Greek Yogurt and increase the Protein of your meal)
- 4-8 High-Fiber Tortilla or Wraps

Depending on if you are meal prepping or how many people you are feeding you may use only one pound of ground beef. Brown the meat and add the taco seasoning and water. Once the taco meat is done, add to your tortilla or wrap and top with guacamole, cheddar and sour cream or Greek yogurt.

A Healthier Taco Wrap	
Servings	1
	Per Serving
Calories	512
Fat g	30
Saturated Fat g	6
Cholesterol mg	21
Carbohydrates g	33
Fiber g	11
Sugar g	5
Protein g	36
Sodium mg	1034

Cilantro Black Bean, Chicken and Lime Quesadilla

THIS IS MADE WITH LEFTOVERS from the Cilantro Lime Crock Pot Chicken Recipe. You only need to buy some high-fiber tortillas.

Ingredients:
- Leftover Cilantro Lime Crock Pot Chicken
- High-Fiber Wraps or Tortillas
- 1 TBS Butter

Microwave leftover cilantro lime chicken. Place butter in frying pan and bring to medium heat. Place wrap/tortilla in pan at low heat and flip as it begins to get crispy and toasty. Spoon leftover cilantro lime chicken into wrap/tortilla and fold in half making a half moon shape. Flip so each side is crunchy. Remove from heat. Optionally top with sour cream, guacamole, hot sauce or whatever suits your fancy. See crock pot recipe elsewhere in this book for nutrition facts and be sure to add in calories from tortilla or wrap.

Dinner

Naked Fajitas

Ingredients:
- 12 Ounces Chicken Breast
- 1 Cup Fresh Portabella Mushrooms
- ½ Vidalia Onion
- 3 Sweet Bell Peppers
- 1 Pack Fajita Seasoning
- 2 Cups Fresh Lettuce

Grill chicken and peppers. Yes, grill the peppers. Just wash them and put them right on the grill. Once the chicken is done, remove along with the peppers. Slice the chicken, onion and peppers into strips. Combine peppers, chicken, sliced onion and mushrooms in saucepan with fajita seasoning (follow fajita instructions) and Sauté.

Serve on lettuce instead of tortillas.

Naked Fajitas	
Servings	3
	Per Serving
Calories	314
Fat g	6
Saturated Fat g	1
Cholesterol mg	94
Carbohydrates g	24
Fiber g	6
Sugar g	12
Protein g	41
Sodium mg	188

Homemade Burgers

Ingredients:
- 2 Pounds Lean Ground Beef
- ½ Vidalia Onion
- 2 TBS Worcestershire Sauce
- 1 Tsp. Salt
- Pepper
- 2 Eggs
- ½ Cup Quick Oatmeal

Peel and chop the onion. Place ground beef in large bowl. Add eggs, 1/2 cup of oatmeal, salt, pepper and 2 TBS Worcestershire sauce. Mix, knead and form patties. Grill, broil or cook on stovetop.

Homemade Burgers	
Servings	8
	Per Serving
Calories	133
Fat g	6
Saturated Fat g	2
Cholesterol mg	79
Carbohydrates g	6
Fiber g	1
Sugar g	1
Protein g	14
Sodium mg	95

Turkey Burgers

Ingredients:
- 2 Pounds 99% Lean Ground Turkey Breast
- 2 Eggs
- ½ Vidalia Onion
- 2 TBS Worcestershire Sauce
- Salt
- Pepper
- ½ Cup Panko

Combine all ingredients in large bowl, mix, make patties and grill.

Turkey Burgers	
Servings	8
	Per Serving
Calories	100
Fat g	2
Saturated Fat g	0
Cholesterol mg	81
Carbohydrates g	5
Fiber g	0
Sugar g	1
Protein g	16
Sodium mg	96

Cashew-Crusted Halibut

Ingredients:
- 1 Pound Halibut Filets
- 2 Cups Panko
- 4 Ounces Cashews
- 4 TBS Parmesan Cheese
- 1 TSP each of Rosemary, Thyme and Oregano
- 1 TBS Butter

Cashew-crusted halibut looks gourmet and is easy to make. The hardest thing to locate for most will be fresh halibut.

Run the cashews through the food processor. Use the pulse button and do not get carried away turning the nuts into powder. Mix the panko, nuts, parmesan and herbs in a bowl. Wash the halibut. Pour the panko-nut mix onto a plate. Press the fish onto the mix. Flip and do the same thing on the other side. Some recipes call for dipping the fish in eggs, milk or some combo thereof. This is not necessary.

Melt 1 TBS of butter in a cast-iron oven safe pot. Heat the oven to 350F. Place fish in cast-iron pot and bake for 15-20 minutes. Since ovens vary, you may need to bake longer or at a higher temp. The fish will flake apart when done.

Optionally, serve with roasted parmesan red potatoes and a white sauce.

Cashew-Crusted Halibut	
Servings	4
	Per Serving
Calories	454
Fat g	19
Saturated Fat g	3
Cholesterol mg	0
Carbohydrates g	41
Fiber g	2
Sugar g	4
Protein g	34
Sodium mg	197

Ingredients:
- 12 Ounces Chicken Breast
- 2 TBS Honey
- 2 TBS Balsamic Vinegar
- 1 Garlic Clove
- 1 Tsp. Basil
- 1 Tsp. Salt

Grill the chicken. Combine the other ingredients in a bowl and brush onto chicken when it is taken off the grill and fully cooked. Creativity goes a long way to breaking up the same old same old with chicken. Check out the spice section of your local grocer or look online. The only limit to your options with chicken is your mind.

Roasted Honey Balsamic Chicken	
Servings	4
	Per Serving
Calories	176
Fat g	3
Saturated Fat g	1
Cholesterol mg	72
Carbohydrates g	10
Fiber g	0
Sugar g	9
Protein g	27
Sodium mg	63

Ingredients:
- 2 Boneless, Skinless Chicken Breasts
- 2 TBS Dijon Mustard
- 2 TBS Honey
- 2 TBS Lemon Juice
- 1 Tsp. Rosemary

Grill or bake the chicken breasts. Mix all of the ingredients. Use a basting brush and coat the chicken breasts. NOTE: Break out of the norm. Add some spice. Check out great grocery stores for spices.

Honey Glazed Chicken	
Servings	4
	Per Serving
Calories	175
Fat g	3
Saturated Fat g	1
Cholesterol mg	72
Carbohydrates g	9
Fiber g	0
Sugar g	8
Protein g	29
Sodium mg	93

Chicken Parmesan with Italian Sausage Gravy

Ingredients:
- 2 Pounds Chicken Breast
- ½ Pound Sweet, Ground Italian Sausage
- 1 Diced, Vidalia Onion
- 4 TBS Parmesan Cheese
- 4 TBS Panko
- 2 Cups of your Favorite Spaghetti Sauce
- 1 TBS Olive Oil

Preheat oven to 400F. Brown the Italian sausage and diced onion and set aside. Mix the parmesan and panko. Dip and flip the chicken in the panko/parm mix. Put olive oil in bottom of oven safe dish. Place chicken in dish and place dish in oven. Bake for 30-40 minutes. In a saucepan combine Italian sausage, onion and spaghetti sauce. Cook and make gravy. Remove chicken from oven and top with gravy. Feel free to top with more parmesan cheese and even some mozzarella cheese. Instead of pasta serve with spaghetti squash or bell peppers. There are great recipes for each in this book.

Chicken Parmesan with Italian Sausage Gravy	
Servings	8
	Per Serving
Calories	242
Fat g	9
Saturated Fat g	2
Cholesterol mg	61
Carbohydrates g	10
Fiber g	2
Sugar g	5
Protein g	31
Sodium mg	873

Seared Tuna Steak

A NICE BREAK FROM THE same old chicken and beef. Tuna. Living in the Midwest great fresh fish can be hit or miss. Much to my surprise, the tuna I bought was a great piece of fish. Check your local grocer and you may be surprised as well.

Ingredients:
- 16 Ounces Fresh Tuna Steak
- 1 TBS Peppercorns
- 2 TBS Butter
- 2 TBS Soy Sauce
- 4 TBS Pickled Ginger
- Optional Baja Mango Salsa

Seared Tuna Steak	
Servings	4
	Per Serving
Calories	162
Fat g	7
Saturated Fat g	5
Cholesterol mg	15
Carbohydrates g	8
Fiber g	0
Sugar g	6
Protein g	23
Sodium mg	766

Place 2 TBS of butter in a frying pan. I used a Lodge cast-iron pan. Set burner to medium heat. Add peppercorns and allow the butter and oil to heat up and soften the peppercorns. Note some of the pepper will pop. Add tuna steak. Cook for 2-3 minutes per side depending on how rare you like the center. Done. Remove steak from heat. Top with soy sauce and pickled ginger. This would pair well with our Baja Mango Salsa.

Margherita Squash with Shrimp

Ingredients:
- 1 Large Spaghetti Squash
- 1 TBS Olive Oil
- 1 Tomato
- 1 Tsp. Oregano
- 1 Tsp. Basil
- ½ Cup Shredded Mozzarella Cheese
- 1 Pound Frozen or Fresh Ready to Eat Shrimp

Add shrimp to Margherita Spaghetti Squash recipe (see page 116) found in this book and increase the protein of this great recipe.

Margherita Squash with Shrimp	
Servings	4
	Per Serving
Calories	192
Fat g	7
Saturated Fat g	2
Cholesterol mg	8
Carbohydrates g	10
Fiber g	2
Sugar g	4
Protein g	23
Sodium mg	92

Zesty Lime Shrimp And Avocado Salad

Ingredients:
- 1 Pound Frozen (thawed) or Fresh Ready to Eat Shrimp
- 1 Medium Tomato
- 1 Avocado
- 1 Jalapeno Pepper (Optional)
- 1/4 Cup Chopped Onion (Optional)
- 2 Limes
- 1 TBS Olive Oil
- Salt and Pepper

Wash tomato and jalapeno pepper. Dice tomato and avocado. Remove seeds from jalapeno pepper and dice. Chop shrimp. In a small bowl combine onion, lime juice, olive oil, pinch of salt and pepper. Let them marinate at least 5 minutes to mellow the flavor of the onion. Combine and mix all ingredients in one bowl and serve.

Zesty Lime Shrimp and Avocado Salad	
Servings	4
	Per Serving
Calories	161
Fat g	8
Saturated Fat g	1
Cholesterol mg	0
Carbohydrates g	6
Fiber g	3
Sugar g	2
Protein g	18
Sodium mg	4

Chopped Chicken and Vegetables

Ingredients:

1 Pound Chicken Breast
½ Cup Shredded Mozzarella Cheese
1.5 Pounds Frozen Mixed Vegetables
½ Cup Spaghetti Sauce
1 TBS Oregano
1 TBS Basil

Grill, bake, or use leftover chicken. Chop, shred or cube the chicken. Place frozen vegetables in pot, top with water, place on stove and bring to boil. Once vegetables are tender, remove from heat, drain water and dust with oregano and basil. Get creative and add some corn and sweet peppers to your vegetable mix. Combine chicken with vegetables and top with shredded mozzarella and spaghetti sauce.

Chopped Chicken and Vegetables	
Servings	4
	Per Serving
Calories	212
Fat g	7
Saturated Fat g	3
Cholesterol mg	68
Carbohydrates g	13
Fiber g	4
Sugar g	5
Protein g	29
Sodium mg	569

Louisiana Andouille Sausage and Riced Cauliflower

Ingredients:

- 12 Ounce Andouille Precooked Chicken Sausage
- 2 Tsp. Paprika
- 1 TBS Olive Oil
- 10-Ounce Bag of Frozen Riced Cauliflower
- 2 Sweet Peppers
- 1 Can Sweet Whole Kernel Corn

Slice sausage. Wash peppers, remove seeds and chop. Drain corn. Follow instructions for cooking on cauliflower bag. Combine remaining vegetables, sausage, olive oil and paprika. Sauté until vegetables are soft. Top riced cauliflower with vegetables and sausage. Salt and pepper to taste.

Louisiana Andouille Sausage and Riced Cauliflower	
Servings	4
	Per Serving
Calories	246
Fat g	17
Saturated Fat g	4
Cholesterol mg	68
Carbohydrates g	19
Fiber g	4
Sugar g	9
Protein g	16
Sodium mg	786

Grilled Chicken and Vegetables

Ingredients:

- 1 Pound Chicken Breast
- 4 Cups Frozen or Fresh Mixed Vegetables
- 1 TBS Olive Oil
- 1 TBS Infused Vinegar
- 2 TBS Light Italian Salad Dressing

Grilled Chicken and Vegetables	
Servings	4
	Per Serving
Calories	164
Fat g	3
Saturated Fat g	1
Cholesterol mg	61
Carbohydrates g	8
Fiber g	2
Sugar g	4
Protein g	24
Sodium mg	413

Marinate chicken breasts overnight in Italian salad dressing. Grill chicken breasts. If using frozen vegetables place frozen vegetables in pot and top with water, place on stove and bring to boil. Once vegetables are tender remove from heat, drain water and add some olive oil and 1-2 TBS Italian dressing. Toss vegetables. If using fresh vegetables, wash, chop and place in frying pan with olive oil. Sauté until vegetables are tender. Remove from heat and add 1-2 TBS Italian dressing and toss. Do NOT use the leftover marinade from the chicken breast. Use fresh dressing for vegetables.

Sirloin Steak Kabobs

Ingredients:

- 16 Ounces Sirloin Steak
- 12 Cherry Tomatoes
- 8 Mushrooms
- 2 Green Peppers
- Bamboo Shish Kabob Skewers

Sirloin Steak Kabobs	
Servings	4
	Per Serving
Calories	212
Fat g	12
Saturated Fat g	5
Cholesterol mg	40
Carbohydrates g	7
Fiber g	3
Sugar g	3
Protein g	18
Sodium mg	55

Cube Steak. Wash vegetables and cut up green peppers. Stick the steak and vegetables on the skewers and then grill. Get creative and use any vegetables you want as well as any cut of steak. Don't pack the meat and vegetables real tight or it will take longer to cook. Also, bamboo skewers are much better than regular ones so look for bamboo.

Ingredients:

- 16 Ounces Chicken Breast
- 2 Sweet Peppers
- 1 Sweet Onion
- Spices, Garlic, Oregano, Mixed Grilling Spice
- 1 TBS Olive Oil
- 2 TBS Light Italian Salad Dressing
- Bamboo Shish Kabob Skewers

Using chef scissors (not sure what their real name is, but they come with a knife block set), cut and cube the chicken, peppers and assorted vegetables you may use. Skewer the chicken, peppers and any other vegetables. Go chicken-vegetable back and forth. Skewer and put on the grill!

When chicken is cooked remove from the grill, drizzle some olive oil and Italian dressing over them and dust with your favorite spices. Done!

Great way to repurpose your leftover chicken kabobs. Grab your leftovers, if there are any. Strip the chicken and veggies off the skewers with a fork. Slice and dice some onions and some of the peppers you did not cook on day one. Put some olive oil in a frying pan. Add the vegetables and sliced chicken. Boom, done.

Chicken Kabobs	
Servings	4
	Per Serving
Calories	180
Fat g	7
Saturated Fat g	1
Cholesterol mg	61
Carbohydrates g	7
Fiber g	2
Sugar g	4
Protein g	23
Sodium mg	409

Ingredients:
- 16 Ounces Chicken Breast
- 4 Sweet Peppers
- 2 Cups Fresh Green Beans
- 1 TBS Fresh Garlic
- 1 TBS Oregano
- 1 TBS Olive Oil

Wash peppers. Grill chicken and peppers. Wash and steam green beans. Toss beans in oil and oregano. Top with grilled chicken and peppers.

Chicken, Peppers and Green Beans	
Servings	4
	Per Serving
Calories	209
Fat g	7
Saturated Fat g	1
Cholesterol mg	61
Carbohydrates g	12
Fiber g	5
Sugar g	6
Protein g	25
Sodium mg	291

Chicken and Ginger Lime Asparagus

Ingredients:
- 2 Pounds Chicken Breast
- 20 Spears Fresh Asparagus
- 1 TBS Lime-Infused Olive Oil
- 2 TBS Honey Ginger Infused Vinegar

Grill or bake the chicken breast. Wash asparagus then trim the ends. Place asparagus in aluminum foil and top with 1 TBS of lime-infused olive oil and 2 TBS of Honey Ginger Infused Vinegar. Grill the asparagus until stalks are tender. Remove from grill or oven and enjoy.

Chicken and Ginger Lime Asparagus	
Servings	4
	Per Serving
Calories	188
Fat g	8
Saturated Fat g	2
Cholesterol mg	61
Carbohydrates g	6
Fiber g	2
Sugar g	2
Protein g	23
Sodium mg	301

Carved Chicken, Chipped Sweet Potato and Spiralized Cucumber Salad

Ingredients:

- ○ 16 Ounces Chicken Breast
- ○ 1 Large Sweet Potato
- ○ 2 Cucumbers
- ○ 1 TBS Olive Oil
- ○ 2 TBS Vinegar
- ○ Salt and Pepper

Grill the chicken breasts. Wash the sweet potato and cucumbers. Peel the cucumbers. To chip the sweet potato use a vegetable spiralizer. We have and use the Veggetti brand. Preheat oven to 250F and bake chips on foil-covered cookie sheet until crispy and browned. Top with salt. Spiralize the cucumber. Place cucumber in large bowl and top with 1 TBS olive oil and 2 TBS vinegar. Mix, toss and salt/pepper to taste.

Carved Chicken, Chipped Sweet Potato and Spiralized Cucumber Salad	
Servings	4
	Per Serving
Calories	216
Fat g	7
Saturated Fat g	1
Cholesterol mg	61
Carbohydrates g	15
Fiber g	2
Sugar g	6
Protein g	23
Sodium mg	319

Naked Burger and Vegetables

Ingredients:

- 2 Pounds of Lean Ground Beef
- 3-4 Cups Frozen Mixed Vegetables
- 2 TBS Parmesan Cheese

Make ¼ pound to ½ burger patties. Check out our burger recipe or use your own. Grill patties. Place frozen vegetables in pot, top with water, place on stove and bring to boil. Once vegetables are tender remove from heat, drain water and dust with parmesan cheese.

Naked Burger and Vegetables	
Servings	4
	Per Serving
Calories	221
Fat g	9
Saturated Fat g	3
Cholesterol mg	64
Carbohydrates g	7
Fiber g	2
Sugar g	3
Protein g	26
Sodium mg	124

Grilled Steak and Vegetables

Ingredients:
- ○ 16 Ounces Sirloin Steak
- ○ 4 Cups Frozen Vegetables
- ○ 2 TBS parmesan Cheese
- ○ Salt
- ○ Pepper

Grill steaks. One minute before re-moving steak from grill, top with one TBS of butter and dust with parmesan cheese, salt and pepper. Place frozen vegetables in pot, top with water, place on stove and bring to boil. Once vegetables are tender take off heat, drain water and dust with parmesan cheese.

Grilled Steak and Vegetables	
Servings	4
	Per Serving
Calories	261
Fat g	13
Saturated Fat g	5
Cholesterol mg	82
Carbohydrates g	7
Fiber g	2
Sugar g	3
Protein g	26
Sodium mg	114

Low-Carb Rice-Free Asian Chicken

Ingredients:

- ○ 10-Ounce Bag Frozen Riced Cauliflower
- ○ 16 Ounces Chicken Breast
- ○ ½ Cup Peas
- ○ 1 Cup Shredded Carrots
- ○ Soy Sauce (Low Sodium if of concern)

You can make a variety of your favorite Asian cuisine without the rice by using riced cauliflower. Check the frozen section of your local grocery store. Cook riced cauliflower per the package instructions. You could also start with fresh cauliflower and make your own. Bake or grill your chicken breast. You could also use leftover chicken breast. Heat peas and carrots, then combine with the riced cauliflower. Top with chicken and your favorite soy sauce to taste.

Low-Carb Rice-Free Asian Chicken	
Servings	4
	Per Serving
Calories	168
Fat g	6
Saturated Fat g	3
Cholesterol mg	68
Carbohydrates g	12
Fiber g	4
Sugar g	6
Protein g	25
Sodium mg	381

Italian Sausage, Spinach and Peppers

YOU KNOW THAT LOOKS GREAT! Italian sausage, peppers, tomatoes, mozzarella...big on taste! Plus it can be healthy if you use one of the lower-fat sausages.

Ingredients:

- 1 Package of Five Sweet or Hot Italian Sausages
- 2 Tomatoes
- 1 Sweet Onion
- 1 TBS Olive Oil
- Balsamic Vinegar
- 4 Sweet Peppers
- 2 Cups Spinach

Italian Sausage, Spinach and Peppers	
Servings	4
	Per Serving
Calories	540
Fat g	36
Saturated Fat g	14
Cholesterol mg	83
Carbohydrates g	27
Fiber g	10
Sugar g	14
Protein g	32
Sodium mg	997

Grill the sausage. Wash the peppers and toss them on the grill too. Grilled peppers are great-tasting and easy to prepare.

Slice your tomatoes. Peel and slice the onion. Sauté the onions and tomatoes. Remove the peppers from the grill, core, slice and sauté. Remove the sausage from the grill, slice and combine all of the vegetables in one frying or sauté pan. Simmer on low heat. Serve, enjoy!

Ingredients:
- 2 Pounds Lean Ground Beef
- 3-5 Peppers
- 1 Cup Fat-Free Plain Greek Yogurt
- Cheddar Cheese
- Taco Seasoning

Wash the peppers, brown and drain the meat, add the taco seasoning per instructions on packet. Core the peppers. Put cheese in the bottom of the peppers. Fill with ground beef. Top with more cheese and yogurt. Go nuts with salsa, hot sauce and anything else you can think of!

Low Carb Your Taco	
Servings	4
	Per Serving
Calories	315
Fat g	13
Saturated Fat g	6
Cholesterol mg	75
Carbohydrates g	17
Fiber g	6
Sugar g	10
Protein g	35
Sodium mg	186

Wasabi Steak Salad

Ingredients:
- 16 Ounces Flank Steak
- 2 Cups Broccoli Cole Slaw
- 1 Cup Shredded Carrots
- Wasabi Dijon Dressing
- 4 Cups Spring Mix (Arugula, Spinach, etc.)

Grill, broil or cook steak on the stove top to your desired finish. Toss broccoli slaw and spring mix together. Slice steak thin and place on top of mixed vegetables. Drizzle wasabi or similar dressing to your liking. Pairs well with quinoa and cucumber salad.

Wasabi Steak Salad	
Servings	4
	Per Serving
Calories	236
Fat g	10
Saturated Fat g	5
Cholesterol mg	55
Carbohydrates g	8
Fiber g	3
Sugar g	4
Protein g	26
Sodium mg	160

Foil Pack Andouille Sausage and Vegetables

Ingredients:

- 1 Red, Orange and Yellow Sweet Peppers
- 1 Vidalia Onion
- 10 Small Red Potatoes
- 1 Package Chicken or Turkey Sausage (look for the fully cooked; it will save cook time)
- Sea salt
- Ground Pepper
- 2 Tsp. Paprika
- 2 Cloves of Garlic, Pressed
- 1 TBS Oregano
- 2 TBS Olive Oil
- Aluminum Foil

Wash, core and cut the peppers and remove the seeds. Chop or slice to your preference.

Peel and chop the onion. Wash and microwave potatoes for four minutes. Cut the potatoes into small cubes. Leave the skin or remove depending on taste. Cube the sausage.

Preheat the grill to medium heat. (Can also bake in the oven at 350-400 F for 30 minutes)

Combine the olive oil, oregano, garlic, paprika, season to taste with salt and pepper in a large bowl and mix well. Place meat, vegetables and seasoning mix in large bowl and mix. Be sure to fully coat everything.

Fill foil packs with meat and spice mix. Tip: you can make extra to grill or bake at a later time. Put a generous amount of the mixture in the center of a piece of foil and then fold up the first piece of foil and then the next piece of foil to form a secure pocket. Grill covered over medium heat for 10-15 minutes (depending on heat of grill) until veggies are crisp-tender.

Foil Pack Andouille Sausage and Vegetables	
Servings	4
	Per Serving
Calories	261
Fat g	17
Saturated Fat g	3
Cholesterol mg	60
Carbohydrates g	17
Fiber g	2
Sugar g	3
Protein g	14
Sodium mg	604

Ingredients:

- 4 Individual Marinated Salmon
- 2 Cucumbers
- 12 Cherry Tomatoes
- Plain Greek Yogurt
- 2 TBS Toasted Sesame Oil
- 2 TBS Balsamic Vinegar
- 2 Sweet Potatoes

Why Uncle Bud's? Because Bud turned me on to these great salmon filets. This is a great meal that takes a half hour or less to prepare. Grilled salmon and sweet potatoes with sides of cucumber in Greek yogurt, yes yogurt and cucumber with cherry tomatoes.

Sweet potatoes off the grill taste great but they take FOREVER to cook on the grill. Here is how to speed up the grilling time. So wash them, then microwave them for 5 minutes. From the microwave place the potatoes into some foil and onto the grill.

Next place the salmon on a sheet of foil and then the foil onto the grill. The salmon used was from one of the warehouse stores. They come pre-marinated and are great because you can pull out how many you need from the freezer, let them thaw and then cook. No need to season or anything. Grill for 20 minutes or until fish will flake with your fork.

Wash everything. Peel and slice the cucumber. Slice the cherry tomatoes in half. Combine the cherry tomatoes and cucumber in a bowl. Pour oil and balsamic over, cover with lid and shake. If you do not have a lid, mix with a large serving spoon. Refrigerate until food comes off the grill.

Take another cucumber. Slice and put in bowl. Top with 1 cup of plain Greek yogurt. This is a great way to up the protein content of your side. It is a modern, high-protein play on the old cucumber-and-sour cream recipe.

Uncle Bud's Salmon, Sweet Potato and Cucumber	
Servings	4
	Per Serving
Calories	312
Fat g	15
Saturated Fat g	4
Cholesterol mg	30
Carbohydrates g	25
Fiber g	4
Sugar g	9
Protein g	22
Sodium mg	195

His and Hers Chili

Ingredients:
- Chili Seasoning
- 1 Pound each of Ground Beef and Venison
- 1 Onion
- Garlic
- Your Favorite Hot Pepper
- 4 TBS Salsa
- 2 Tomatoes

His and Hers Chili	
Servings	4
	Per Serving
Calories	171
Fat g	6
Saturated Fat g	2
Cholesterol mg	50
Carbohydrates g	6
Fiber g	1
Sugar g	2
Protein g	24
Sodium mg	120

OK, this is called "His and Hers" because both venison and beef chili are going to be made. Brown the beef and venison. Drain the grease and put back on the stove. Something different. Dice, slice or chop onion and tomatoes. Brown the onion. Follow the directions on the chili seasoning packet. Add the onions, tomatoes and some garlic too. As a bonus to the "His" chili one hot pepper was washed, cored and added whole to simmer in the pot.

Shredded Chicken Ranch Tacos

Ingredients:
- 2 Pounds Boneless, Skinless Chicken Breast
- 1 Packet Ranch Dressing Mix
- 1 Packet Taco Seasoning
- 1 Cube Chicken Bouillon

Wash and put the chicken in the crock pot. Dump the ranch and taco packets in. Drop one bouillon cube in. Add 1-1.5 cups of water. Cook on low for 5-6 hours or until done. When done the chicken will shred very easily. Shred with spatula and fork. Serve on your favorite high-fiber tortillas or taco shells.

Shredded Chicken Ranch Tacos	
Servings	4
	Per Serving
Calories	251
Fat g	5
Saturated Fat g	2
Cholesterol mg	140
Carbohydrates g	14
Fiber g	0
Sugar g	0
Protein g	40
Sodium mg	1900

Crock Pot Italian Sausage and Peppers

Ingredients:
- 2 Pounds Italian Sausage
- 4 Sweet Peppers 1 Green, 1 Red, 1 Yellow and 1 Orange
- 2 Cups Spaghetti Sauce
- ½ Cup Parmesan Cheese
- 1 Cup Mozzarella Cheese

Crock pots make life easy. Load up your meat, vegetables and any other ingredients. Turn on and let it cook all day while at work or ushering kids around. Crock pot Italian sausage, peppers and tomato sauce. The best part is it is ready and warm when you are ready to eat!

Wash the peppers, core, remove seeds, slice and dice. Put peppers, sausage and sauce in crock pot. Set on low for 5-6 hours. Go to work, run errands or just plain live life. Come back in 5-6 hours and your meal is ready. Top with parmesan and or mozzarella. Dunzo!

Crock Pot Italian Sausage and Peppers	
Servings	8
	Per Serving
Calories	568
Fat g	39
Saturated Fat g	16
Cholesterol mg	114
Carbohydrates g	19
Fiber g	5
Sugar g	12
Protein g	34
Sodium mg	1467

Crock Pot Chicken Enchilada Soup

Ingredients:

- 1 Pound Chicken Breast
- 2 Cups Chicken Stock
- 10 Ounces Red Enchilada Sauce
- 14 Ounce Can Black Beans
- 1 Can Corn
- 4 Ounce Diced Green Chiles
- 2 Cloves of Garlic
- 1 White Onion
- 1 Chicken Bouillon Cubes
- 1 Tsp. Salt

Drain and wash beans. Drain corn. Mince two cloves of garlic. Peel and dice the onion. Toss everything into the crock pot or slow cooker. Cook on low for 6-8 hours….or high for half as much time. Get creative and try some of these extras. You can really get nuts here. Go with what you have in the house already; chopped fresh cilantro, diced avocado, diced red onion, shredded cheese, sour cream, tortilla strips/chips all make great additions. Be sure to account for anything you add to the recipe in terms of nutrition information as it is not included below.

Crock Pot Chicken Enchilada Soup	
Servings	4
	Per Serving
Calories	302
Fat g	3
Saturated Fat g	1
Cholesterol mg	70
Carbohydrates g	38
Fiber g	9
Sugar g	3
Protein g	30
Sodium mg	1683

Ingredients:
- 2 Pounds Chicken Breast
- 1 Cup Salsa
- 2 TBS Taco Seasoning
- 1 Onion
- 3 TBS Sour Cream
- 1 Bag Tortilla Chips (Optional)

Place the chicken in a crock pot or slow cooker. Sprinkle the taco seasoning over the meat then layer the vegetables and salsa on top. Pour a half-cup water over the mixture, do not use too much water! Set on low and cook for 6-8 hours. The meat is cooked when it shreds or reaches an internal temperature of 165°F. When ready to serve, break up or shred the chicken with two forks then stir in the sour cream.

This is one of my absolute favorite meals. Easy to make and so versatile you can use it in a number of different ways all week long!

Repurpose leftovers and turn salsa chicken into a meal by doing any of the following:
Serve as a wrap
Serve over brown rice
Serve in a salad
Use tortilla chips as a spoon
Just eat it cold and your protein and veggie servings are covered!

Crock Pot Salsa Chicken	
Servings	4
	Per Serving
Calories	281
Fat g	8
Saturated Fat g	4
Cholesterol mg	145
Carbohydrates g	13
Fiber g	3
Sugar g	5
Protein g	43
Sodium mg	1412

Easy Crock Pot Chicken

Ingredients:
- 2 Pounds Chicken Breast
- 2 Cups Chicken Stock (or 2 Chicken Bullion Cubes and 2 Cups of Water)
- Salt and pepper to taste
- 1 Clove of Garlic

Combine all of the above in crock pot and cook on low for 6 hours. This is a great way to meal-prep for the week. Make this on Sunday and you are set for most of your work week. Repurpose in wraps, tacos and more!

Easy Crock Pot Chicken	
Servings	4
	Per Serving
Calories	210
Fat g	5
Saturated Fat g	2
Cholesterol mg	140
Carbohydrates g	1
Fiber g	0
Sugar g	1
Protein g	42
Sodium mg	290

Cheesy Chicken and Rice

Ingredients:
- 1 Pound Boneless Skinless Chicken Breast
- 1 Can Cream of Mushroom Soup
- 1 Box Yellow Rice
- 1 Cup Shredded Cheddar Cheese
- 1 Can Whole Corn
- 1 Onion
- 1 Green Pepper

Place chicken in the bottom of crock pot. Peel and dice onion and add to crock pot. Wash, core, remove seeds then chop green pepper and add. Pour soup on top of vegetables and place lid on top of crock pot. Cook on low for 5-6 hours or on high for 3-4 hours. 30 minutes before the chicken is done, cook the rice. When chicken is finished cooking, shred the chicken using two forks and add in cheese, corn and rice. Follow the directions on the box. Mix rice in to crock pot and done.

Cheesy Chicken and Rice	
Servings	4
	Per Serving
Calories	469
Fat g	16
Saturated Fat g	8
Cholesterol mg	103
Carbohydrates g	47
Fiber g	4
Sugar g	2
Protein g	34
Sodium mg	1226

Cilantro Lime Crock Pot Chicken

Ingredients:

- 2 Pounds Chicken Breast
- 2 Limes
- 1 Bunch of Fresh Cilantro
- 1 Can of Corn
- 1 Clove of Garlic
- 1 Sweet Onion
- 1 Can of Black Beans
- Salt
- Pepper

Cilantro Lime Crock Pot Chicken	
Servings	4
	Per Serving
Calories	371
Fat g	49
Saturated Fat g	28
Cholesterol mg	400
Carbohydrates g	128
Fiber g	34
Sugar g	6
Protein g	141
Sodium mg	872

Cilantro Lime Crock Pot or Slow Cook Chicken is a great meal that you can prep in advance and cook later. It is great in tacos or as a meal with a couple of your favorite sides. This means that on the busiest of days you can have a fresh, warm meal waiting for you and your family when you get home from the busy day.

Prep to make later.

Prep Day:
Place chicken in gallon-size freezer bag. Squeeze juice of both limes in. Peel and chop red onion and place half in the bag. Drain and rinse black beans and add to bag. Drain corn and add to bag. Mince one clove of garlic. Add garlic, a dash of salt and pepper then seal the bag and place in the freezer flat.

Cooking Day:
Thaw overnight the day before cooking.

Place contents of bag into a crock pot and cook on low for eight hours. Shred and add fresh cilantro to taste.

Ingredients:
- 2 Pounds Chuck Roast Stew Meat
- 1 Can Condensed French Onion Soup (Buy the Name Brand)
- 1 Cup Shredded Cheddar Cheese
- 1 TBS Chili Powder
- 1 Tsp. Paprika
- 1 Bunch Cilantro

This recipe can be prepared the day of or made in advance and frozen and made later.

Prep Day:
Place chili powder and paprika in small bag and do not freeze them. Place cheddar cheese in small bag. Put chuck roast in a large freezer bag. Place cheese and roast in freezer.

Cooking Day:
Remove frozen food from freezer and allow to thaw. Pour condensed soup, paprika and chili powder in crock pot. Add chuck roast. Make sure to coat with soup and spice well. Cook on low for 6-8 hours. Beef should be tender and pull apart with a fork when done. Use two forks to shred chuck roast in crock pot. Add in cilantro to taste. Top with cheddar cheese and serve on high-fiber tortillas. Go naked and skip the tortilla and place in a bowl and pair with your favorite vegetables. Tortillas not included in nutrition info.

Shredded Beef Crock Pot Tacos	
Servings	6
	Per Serving
Calories	460
Fat g	180
Saturated Fat g	82
Cholesterol mg	877
Carbohydrates g	50
Fiber g	4
Sugar g	30
Protein g	259
Sodium mg	686

Salad

Cucumber Tomato Salad

Ingredients:
- 2 Large Cucumbers
- 1 Vidalia Onion
- 2 Tomatoes
- 2 TBS Infused Honey Ginger Balsamic Vinegar
- 1 TBS Infused Lime Olive Oil

Wash cucumbers and tomatoes, peel cucumber, cube/quarter/eighth the tomato, peel/cube/quarter/eighth the onion, combine in bowl. Top with Lime Olive Oil and Honey Ginger Balsamic Vinegar....then refrigerate. For some reason this tastes best chilled.

Cucumber Tomato Salad	
Servings	4
	Per Serving
Calories	84
Fat g	5
Saturated Fat g	1
Cholesterol mg	0
Carbohydrates g	11
Fiber g	2
Sugar g	4
Protein g	1
Sodium mg	6

Watermelon, Blueberry, Feta and Mint Salad

Ingredients:
- 6 Cups Ripe Watermelon
- 1 Cup Blueberries
- ½ Cup Mint Leaves
- 3 Ounces Crumbled Feta Cheese
- 1 TBS Olive Oil
- 1 TBS Balsamic Vinegar

Cut the watermelon into chunks and remove the rind. Toss watermelon in oil and vinegar. Shred the mint leaves. Experiment with some of the great tasting infused vinegars. Top watermelon with berries, mint and crumbled feta.

Watermelon, Blueberry, Feta and Mint Salad	
Servings	4
	Per Serving
Calories	175
Fat g	7
Saturated Fat g	3
Cholesterol mg	11
Carbohydrates g	24
Fiber g	1
Sugar g	18
Protein g	6
Sodium mg	258

Tomato and Spinach Salad

Ingredients:
- 12 Cherry Tomatoes
- 4 Cups Spinach
- 1 TBS Olive Oil
- 2 TBS Balsamic Vinegar

What do you do with all of those tomatoes from the garden? Get creative. Spinach and tomato salad is quick and painless to make. Wash the tomatoes and spinach. Quarter the tomatoes and combine with spinach in large bowl. Top with olive oil and vinegar. Optionally top with fresh grated parmesan cheese, garlic and crushed black pepper. Done!

Tomato and Spinach Salad	
Servings	4
	Per Serving
Calories	51
Fat g	4
Saturated Fat g	1
Cholesterol mg	0
Carbohydrates g	5
Fiber g	1
Sugar g	3
Protein g	1
Sodium mg	26

Cucumber Onion Salad

Ingredients:

- 2 Cucumbers
- 1 Sweet Onion
- 1 TBS Olive Oil
- 2 TBS Apple Cider or Balsamic Vinegar

Slice the cucumbers. Wash them first, of course. Leave the skin on or peel them, up to you. Slice and chop the onion. Combine all ingredients in large bowl and toss. Dash some salt and a little pepper and you are done. Cover and place in the fridge for 15-20 minutes.

Cucumber Onion Salad	
Servings	4
	Per Serving
Calories	59
Fat g	4
Saturated Fat g	1
Cholesterol mg	0
Carbohydrates g	9
Fiber g	2
Sugar g	5
Protein g	29
Sodium mg	34

Sides

Carnival Squash

Ingredients:
- 1 Carnival Squash
- 1 TBS Butter
- 1 TBS Olive Oil

This is carnival squash. Probably the coolest-looking of the squash.... What do you do with these things though? Same as the rest of the squash. Yes, their seeds are edible as well.

Wash the squash. Cut and remove the seeds... save the seeds as you can bake and eat them too. Melt butter in the microwave or better yet as the oven is warming to 350 F, set the butter in a bowl on top of the oven...it will melt in a hurry. Mix the olive oil and butter. Brush the oil and butter onto the squash. Place the squash face down on a foil-covered baking sheet. Bake for 20-30 minute or until a fork can easily pierce the squash. Remove from the oven and use a fork and spoon to remove the meat of the squash from the skin. Each serving is ¾ cup.

Carnival Squash	
Servings	4
	Per Serving
Calories	116
Fat g	10
Saturated Fat g	3
Cholesterol mg	8
Carbohydrates g	7
Fiber g	1
Sugar g	3
Protein g	1
Sodium mg	21

Delicata Squash

Ingredients:
- 4 Cups Delicata Squash
- 2 TBS Butter
- 1 TBS Olive Oil
- Salt
- Black Pepper
- 4 TBS Parmesan Cheese

Wash the squash. Slice into rings. Melt the butter (in microwave or on stove top) and combine with olive oil. Brush oil and butter or better yet dip the rings into the butter-olive oil combo. Put foil on a cookie sheet. Place rings on cookie sheet. Place in oven at 350-400F for 15-30 minutes or until soft and can be cut with fork. Remove and dust with salt, pepper and parmesan.

Delicata Squash	
Servings	4
	Per Serving
Calories	136
Fat g	11
Saturated Fat g	3
Cholesterol mg	8
Carbohydrates g	10
Fiber g	1
Sugar g	4
Protein g	1
Sodium mg	58

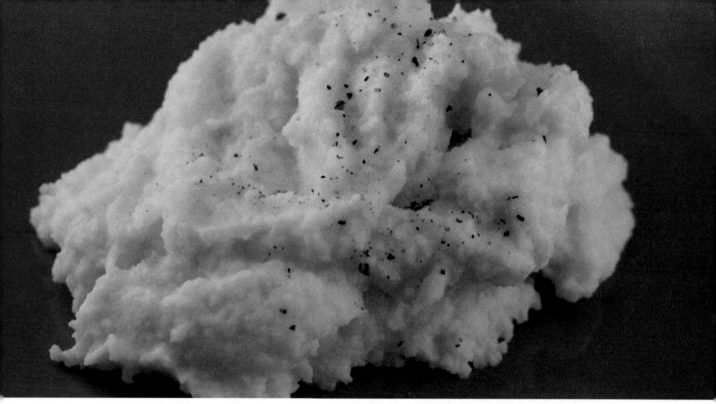

Garlic Mashed Cauliflower

Ingredients:
- 1 Medium Head Cauliflower
- 1 TBS Butter
- 4 TBS Sour Cream
- 4 Garlic Cloves
- Black Pepper
- Water

Garlic Mashed Cauliflower	
Servings	4
	Per Serving
Calories	96
Fat g	6
Saturated Fat g	4
Cholesterol mg	14
Carbohydrates g	8
Fiber g	4
Sugar g	4
Protein g	3
Sodium mg	71

Wash, cut and chop cauliflower into small pieces. Add water and cauliflower to large pot. Use a garlic press on the garlic and add to the water. Bring to a boil and boil for fifteen minutes or until cauliflower is tender. Drain broth. Add to food processor and process to mashed potato consistency.

A faster Garlic Mashed Cauliflower.

Use the microwaved riced cauliflower (instructions are on the bag) and a handheld Braun-style mixer. 1 bag of riced cauliflower, fresh garlic, 1 TBS butter, 2 TBS sour cream. Microwave the cauliflower and then combine all ingredients in mixing bowl and mix with the Braun-style mixer. Took about 10 minutes and made about 4 servings.

115

Margherita Spaghetti Squash

Ingredients:

- 1 Large Spaghetti Squash
- 1 TBS Olive Oil
- 1 Tomato
- 1 Tsp. Oregano
- 1 Tsp. Basil
- ½ Cup Shredded Mozzarella Cheese

Margherita Spaghetti Squash	
Servings	4
	Per Serving
Calories	122
Fat g	7
Saturated Fat g	2
Cholesterol mg	8
Carbohydrates g	10
Fiber g	2
Sugar g	4
Protein g	6
Sodium mg	92

Preheat the oven to 350F. Wash squash. Cut spaghetti squash lengthwise and remove seeds. Brush squash with olive oil. Place in oven safe dish and bake for 40 minutes. Use a fork to pull the squash out in strands like spaghetti noodles. Wash and dice tomato and place tomato, oil and spices in oven safe dish. Place dish in oven to heat for the last 10 minutes the squash is in the oven. Top squash with tomatoes, seasoning and cheese.

Caprese Tomato Mozzarella

Ingredients:

- 1 Medium Tomato
- 1 Fresh Mozzarella Cheese Ball
- 1 Vidalia Onion (optional)
- Basil
- Oregano
- 1 TBS Olive Oil
- 2 TBS Balsamic Vinegar

Wash and slice the tomatoes, slice the mozzarella, stack on the plate and dash with herbs. Drizzle oil and vinegar over the top.

Caprese Tomato Mozzarella	
Servings	2
	Per Serving
Calories	201
Fat g	16
Saturated Fat g	7
Cholesterol mg	0
Carbohydrates g	5
Fiber g	1
Sugar g	4
Protein g	10
Sodium mg	204

Parmesan Crusted Potatoes

Ingredients:

- 10 Small Red Potatoes
- 2 Tsp. Thyme
- 4 TBS Parmesan Cheese
- 1 Tsp. Garlic Salt
- 1 TBS Olive Oil

Parmesan Crusted Potatoes	
Servings	2
	Per Serving
Calories	190
Fat g	9
Saturated Fat g	2
Cholesterol mg	0
Carbohydrates g	23
Fiber g	3
Sugar g	1
Protein g	3
Sodium mg	80

Wash the potatoes and then microwave them for 6 minutes. If time permits they could be cooked on the grill but be prepared to wait, and wait and wait for them to be done. Remove the potatoes and slice thin. Put some olive oil in a cast-iron frying pan and place on low heat. Add the sliced potatoes, thyme (to taste) and dust with garlic salt. Sauté until the potatoes are soft. Remove from heat and sprinkle parmesan cheese on and toss with serving spoon.

Grilled Asparagus

Ingredients:
- 24 Spears of Fresh Asparagus
- 2 TBS Infused Honey Ginger Balsamic
- 1 TBS Infused Persian Lime Olive Oil

Wash and trim the asparagus. Put asparagus on aluminum foil, top with oil and vinegar, fold, crimp edges of foil and grill for 30 minutes or until asparagus is tender. Can also be baked in the oven at 350F. Note oven bake times and temperatures will vary.

Grilled Asparagus	
Servings	4
	Per Serving
Calories	55
Fat g	4
Saturated Fat g	1
Cholesterol mg	0
Carbohydrates g	5
Fiber g	1
Sugar g	3
Protein g	2
Sodium mg	0

Acorn Squash

Ingredients:
- 2 Acorn Squash
- 1 TBS Olive Oil
- Salt and Black Pepper to taste
- 2 TBS Parmesan Cheese

There are a ton of things you can do with squash. Best part: the whole thing is edible...even the seeds (see seed recipe elsewhere in this book).

Wash the squash. Cut in half length-wise. Then use a large spoon to remove the seeds. Remember: keep the seeds because you can eat those too. Preheat oven to 400F. Baste top and bottom of the squash with olive oil. Use one of those fancy basting brushes. Place squash face down on foil-covered cookie sheet. Put cookie sheet into the oven for 25-40 minutes. They are done when soft and a fork or knife can easily push into them. Remove from the oven. Flip over. Dust with salt, pepper and parmesan. Even the skin is edible. If you like the skin, eat it. If not, use your fork or spoon and spoon out the soft insides.

Acorn Squash	
Servings	4
	Per Serving
Calories	131
Fat g	5
Saturated Fat g	1
Cholesterol mg	4
Carbohydrates g	23
Fiber g	3
Sugar g	0
Protein g	3
Sodium mg	63

Watermelon Gazpacho Soup

Ingredients:

- 6 Cups Fresh Watermelon
- 3 Ounces Feta Cheese
- 2 TBS Fresh Dill
- 1 Tomato
- 1 TBS Olive Oil
- ½ Serrano Pepper (optional)
- Salt and Pepper to Taste

Wash, slice and remove seeds from Serrano pepper. Wash and dice the tomato. Slice watermelon and remove rind. Combine pepper, watermelon, dill, tomato and olive oil in a blender and puree. You can also use a hand mixer or food processor. Combine all ingredients in four soup bowls. Garnish with feta and dill.

Watermelon Gazpacho Soup	
Servings	4
	Per Serving
Calories	159
Fat g	7
Saturated Fat g	3
Cholesterol mg	11
Carbohydrates g	20
Fiber g	1
Sugar g	15
Protein g	6
Sodium mg	260

Italian Broccoli

Ingredients:
- 4 Cups Broccoli (fresh or frozen)
- 2 TBS Light or Low Fat Italian Dressing (any brand is fine)

Steam the broccoli. Remove from steamer basket, place in bowl and top with dressing. You do not want to make broccoli soup. Just enough dressing to add some flavor and to un-boring the broccoli. This is a great low-carb side dish that will pair with almost any entree.

Italian Broccoli	
Servings	4
	Per Serving
Calories	65
Fat g	1
Saturated Fat g	0
Cholesterol mg	0
Carbohydrates g	11
Fiber g	3
Sugar g	6
Protein g	3
Sodium mg	38

Sautéed Mini Sweet Peppers

Ingredients:
- Sweet Peppers (One Bag)
- 1 Sweet Onion
- 1 TBS Olive Oil
- Black Pepper to taste
- 2 Cloves Garlic Salt

Wash the peppers, leave the stem and seeds until they are served. Chop the onion and garlic. Sauté everything in olive oil. Dust with black pepper and add some fresh pressed garlic.

Sautéed Mini Sweet Peppers	
Servings	4
	Per Serving
Calories	120
Fat g	4
Saturated Fat g	1
Cholesterol mg	0
Carbohydrates g	19
Fiber g	4
Sugar g	10
Protein g	3
Sodium mg	0

Oven Baked Vegetables

Ingredients:
- 2 Cups Each Cauliflower, Broccoli and Carrots
- 1 TBS of Your Favorite Herb, Spice or Seasoning (Thyme, Rosemary, Basil and Oregano Sound Delish)
- 1 TBS Olive Oil

Preheat oven to 400F. Wash and cut vegetables to bite-sized pieces. Cover baking sheet with aluminum foil. Place vegetables on baking sheet and dust with spices. Be careful not to let them overlap. Bake for 35-45 minutes and flip vegetables halfway through. This can also be done on a grill with a vegetable basket. Just line basket with foil and grill. Remove from oven or grill. Dust with seasonings or spice of your liking. Pour olive oil over the top and mix or toss vegetables. The vegetable options are limitless with this. Red potatoes, sweet peppers and brussel sprouts are all great candidates with this one. Get creative!

Oven Baked Vegetables	
Servings	4
	Per Serving
Calories	71
Fat g	4
Saturated Fat g	1
Cholesterol mg	0
Carbohydrates g	9
Fiber g	4
Sugar g	4
Protein g	3
Sodium mg	52

Zucchini Boats

Ingredients:
- 1 Large Zucchini (about 4 Cups)
- 4 TBS Panko (I had this from previous recipes)
- 1 TBS Italian or Greek Seasoning
- 12 Cherry Tomatoes, Sliced
- 4 TBS Fresh Grated Parmesan
- 1 TBS Olive Oil

Cut the zucchini in half. Use a spoon to core out the center. Mix panko and seasoning. Brush olive oil on the zucchini. Put the zucchini on the grill face down for 8 minutes. Remove zucchini from grill and fill with the panko mix. Top with sliced cherry tomatoes. Grate cheese and put on top. Place back on the grill until the cheese has melted and zucchini is tender. Pairs well with your favorite grilled meat!

Zucchini Boats	
Servings	4
	Per Serving
Calories	128
Fat g	5
Saturated Fat g	2
Cholesterol mg	6
Carbohydrates g	15
Fiber g	4
Sugar g	7
Protein g	8
Sodium mg	107

Higher-Protein Lemon Coleslaw

Ingredients:

- 2 TBS Plain Greek Yogurt
- 2 TBS Sour Cream
- 1 TBS Low-Fat Mayonnaise
- 4 Tsp. Lemon Juice
- 1 Tsp. Sugar
- 3 TBS Water
- 1/4 Tsp. Salt
- 1 Tsp. Black Pepper
- 4 Cups Purple Cabbage
- 1 Cup Carrots

Shred cabbage and carrots in food processor. Alternatively, save time by buying cabbage and carrots already shredded. Whisk together sour cream, yogurt, mayonnaise, lemon juice, sugar, water, salt and pepper in a large bowl until sugar is dissolved. Add cabbage and carrots than toss well. Chill, covered, 1 hour to allow flavors to develop. Season with salt and pepper.

Higher-Protein Lemon Coleslaw	
Servings	4
	Per Serving
Calories	82
Fat g	4
Saturated Fat g	1
Cholesterol mg	2
Carbohydrates g	15
Fiber g	4
Sugar g	8
Protein g	3
Sodium mg	73

5-Minute Cole Slaw

Ingredients:
- 1 Bag Shredded Cabbage
- 1/4 Cup Honey Ginger Balsamic Vinegar
- 3 TBS Organic Lime Olive Oil
- 2 TBS Sugar
- Dash of Salt

Put the cabbage in a bowl. Add the sugar and the salt. Do this now as the liquids will wash them over the cabbage. Add the oil and then finally the vinegar. There are many infused olive oils and vinegars. Try some of them out. Mix in a bowl with a lid that can be securely put on, then shake vigorously. Refrigerate for 15-20 minutes and serve. While the cole slaw is in the fridge make the rest of your dinner.

5-Minute Cole Slaw	
Servings	4
	Per Serving
Calories	142
Fat g	11
Saturated Fat g	2
Cholesterol mg	0
Carbohydrates g	12
Fiber g	2
Sugar g	9
Protein g	1
Sodium mg	24

Protein-Packed Dessert

Key Lime Protein Pie

Ingredients:

- ○ 1 Graham Cracker
- ○ 1 Oikos Triple Zero Lemon Tart Yogurt
- ○ 2 TBS Whipped Cream

Place graham cracker on plate. Top with yogurt and whipped cream and enjoy completely guilt-free! The Oikos Triple Zero has more fiber then most other brands making this a great way to get more daily fiber.

Key Lime Protein Pie	
Servings	1
	Per Serving
Calories	190
Fat g	3
Saturated Fat g	0
Cholesterol mg	5
Carbohydrates g	26
Fiber g	7
Sugar g	10
Protein g	16
Sodium mg	134

Pumpkin Pie Protein

Ingredients:
- 2 Scoops Vanilla Protein Powder
- 1 Can of Pure No Sugar Added Pumpkin
- Pure Ground Cinnamon
- Nutmeg
- Pumpkin Spice
- Allspice

Open the can of pumpkin. Scoop pumpkin from can into a bowl. You can use half the can if you are trying to control carbs. Add two scoops of the vanilla protein powder. Add water and mix until you have a pudding consistency. Add 1 teaspoon of each spice or more to desired taste. Mix well.

Pumpkin Pie Protein	
Servings	2
	Per Serving
Calories	218
Fat g	5
Saturated Fat g	1
Cholesterol mg	15
Carbohydrates g	23
Fiber g	7
Sugar g	11
Protein g	22
Sodium mg	179

Peanut Butter and Jelly Protein Pudding

Ingredients:
- 2 Scoops Strawberry Protein Powder
- 8 Ounces Frozen Mixed Berries without Strawberries (blackberries, blueberries, raspberries)
- 2 TBS Peanut Butter
- Shaker Bottle

Add 2 scoops of protein powder to a shaker bottle, pour in frozen berries and fill the shaker bottle to the top with water. Shake...now it is going to be like shaking concrete. Split contents into two bowls. Get two spoons, scoop out one spoon of peanut butter....mix the peanut butter into your concrete-like mix. Spend the next 10-20 minutes enjoying this high-protein dessert.

Peanut Butter and Jelly Protein Pudding	
Servings	2
	Per Serving
Calories	258
Fat g	11
Saturated Fat g	2
Cholesterol mg	15
Carbohydrates g	17
Fiber g	5
Sugar g	8
Protein g	25
Sodium mg	241

Ingredients:
- 1 Cup Plain Greek Yogurt
- 2 Scoops Cookies and Cream Protein Powder

This un-boring, high-protein Greek yogurt is a great breakfast or snack. Not only is the high-protein Greek yogurt combo fast and convenient, it tastes incredible.

Put 1 cup of Greek yogurt in a bowl. Add two scoops of protein powder. Mix with a spoon, then add water until you have almost a soft-serve ice cream consistency.

Cookies and Cream Protein Yogurt	
Servings	2
	Per Serving
Calories	190
Fat g	3
Saturated Fat g	1
Cholesterol mg	15
Carbohydrates g	9
Fiber g	1
Sugar g	6
Protein g	29
Sodium mg	215

Retro Protein Pudding

Ingredients:
- 2 Scoops Protein Powder
- 4 TBS Heavy Whipping Cream

This is a play on an old favorite of the bodybuilding community. More specifically by Rheo Blair, considered by many as the father of the protein powder industry.

So what is it? A simple, fast and easy high-protein and low-carb meal. Consider it high-protein dessert with no carbs.

Put two scoops of protein powder in a bowl. Pour in the 4 TBS of Heavy Cream. Add a bit of water. Mix to a pudding consistency…enjoy!

Retro Protein Pudding	
Servings	1
	Per Serving
Calories	460
Fat g	26
Saturated Fat g	15
Cholesterol mg	110
Carbohydrates g	10
Fiber g	2
Sugar g	4
Protein g	40
Sodium mg	340

Chocolate Mocha Pudding

Ingredients:
- 2 Scoops Protein Powder
- 1/2 Cup of water
- 3 TBS heavy whipping cream

Handful of coffee beans (ground or you can use coffee grounds)
Combine all ingredients in a bowl. Mix with a spoon, chill and enjoy!

Chocolate Mocha Pudding	
Servings	1
	Per Serving
Calories	410
Fat g	21
Saturated Fat g	11
Cholesterol mg	90
Carbohydrates g	10
Fiber g	2
Sugar g	4
Protein g	40
Sodium mg	340

Ingredients:
- 5 Scoops Chocolate Protein Powder
- 1 Cup Quick Oats
- 1 Cup Your Favorite Peanut Butter
- 1/4 ice cream scooper (kind of like an old-school ice cream scooper used to make cookies found at Bed, Bath and Beyond)
- 1.5 Cups of Water

Combine all ingredients in bowl. A mixer will make this easiest. But you can burn some calories and use a whisk and a spoon. Combine until oats are wet out... so no longer dry.... Cover a cookie sheet with the parchment or wax paper; this prevents the protein balls from sticking to the cookie sheet. Then use the cookie dasher and scoop balls out onto the parchment paper. Place in the refrigerator... lick the spoon and mixer parts... done.

Think outside of the protein shake. No one says that you cannot make high-protein treats that are easy to make and taste great.

Chocolate Peanut Butter Moose Poop	
Servings	12
	Per Serving
Calories	206
Fat g	13
Saturated Fat g	3
Cholesterol mg	6
Carbohydrates g	11
Fiber g	2
Sugar g	3
Protein g	15
Sodium mg	95

Pumpkin Protein Balls

Ingredients:
- 5 Scoops Vanilla Protein Powder
- 1 Cup Quick Oats
- 1 Can Pumpkin (make sure you get the can with no sugar added)
- 2 Tsp. Pure Ground Cinnamon
- 2 Tsp. Nutmeg
- 2 Tsp. Pumpkin Spice
- 1/4 Cookie Dasher (kind of like an old-school ice cream scooper used to make cookies found at your favorite home goods store)

Combine all ingredients in bowl. A mixer will make this easiest. But you can burn some calories and use a whisk and a spoon. Combine until oats and spices are wet out...so no longer dry.... Cover a cookie sheet with the parchment paper, this prevents are pumpkin protein balls from sticking to the cookie sheet. Then use the cookie dasher and scoop balls out onto the parchment paper. Place in the refrigerator...lick the spoon and mixer parts...done.

No one says that you cannot make high protein seasonal treats that are easy to make and taste great. These festive treats are delish and portable.

Pumpkin Protein Balls	
Servings	6
	Per Serving
Calories	188
Fat g	4
Saturated Fat g	1
Cholesterol mg	13
Carbohydrates g	19
Fiber g	4
Sugar g	5
Protein g	19
Sodium mg	185

Protein Popsicles

Ingredients:
- 4 Scoops Protein Powder
- 4 TBS Heavy Whipping Cream
- 1 Cup Plain Greek Yogurt

Blend in a blender or your favorite shaker cup. Fill the popsicle molds and freeze. Tomorrow you will have a great treat. **Each pair of popsicles is going to be around 210 calories and 24 grams of protein and a minimal amount of sugar.** Compare this to the fat-free, high-in-sugar store-bought popsicles!

Limits exist only in our mind. The more creative we can get-the less there are limits. Not sure there is a place more true than when we look at food and food choices. Sometimes it just takes a little creativity to keep eating healthy from getting boring.

Here is an example of that. Protein popsicles. There is no limit to the options with these. Plus…kids LOVE THEM!!! Not only that, but kids enjoy getting involved in making them. This is a great way to start teaching kids how to make better food choices and that good-tasting treats don't need to come out of a box or bag.

Protein Popsicles	
Servings	8
	Per Serving
Calories	105
Fat g	4
Saturated Fat g	2
Cholesterol mg	18
Carbohydrates g	4
Fiber g	1
Sugar g	2
Protein g	12
Sodium mg	96

44
Protein Shake
Recipes

All Protein Shakes are made with 8-12 Ounces of Water to your liking and consistency! The exception are shakes that list milk or almond milk. Mix in blender bottle, blender or similar device.

Ingredients:

- 2 Scoops Chocolate Protein Powder
- 8 Ounces Chocolate Milk or Almond Milk
- 2 TBS Shaved Milk or Dark Chocolate
- 2 TBS Whipped Cream

Triple Chocolate Delight	
Servings	2
	Per Serving
Calories	273
Fat g	12
Saturated Fat g	6
Cholesterol mg	40
Carbohydrates g	15
Fiber g	6
Sugar g	11
Protein g	21
Sodium mg	290

Pumpkin Pie

Ingredients:

- ○ 2 Scoops Vanilla Protein Powder
- ○ 1 TBS Whipping Cream
- ○ 3 Tsp. Cinnamon
- ○ 2 Dashes Nutmeg
- ○ 1/2 Cup Pure Pumpkin (Don't use the Pie Filling use pure pumpkin)

Pumpkin Pie Servings	1
	Per Serving
Calories	360
Fat g	11
Saturated Fat g	4
Cholesterol mg	50
Carbohydrates g	21
Fiber g	5
Sugar g	8
Protein g	42
Sodium mg	355

Peach Cobbler

Ingredients:

- 2 Scoops Vanilla Protein Powder
- 1 TBS Whipping Cream
- 1 Peach
- 3 Tsp. Cinnamon

Peach Cobbler	
Servings	1
	Per Serving
Calories	378
Fat g	11
Saturated Fat g	4
Cholesterol mg	50
Carbohydrates g	27
Fiber g	5
Sugar g	19
Protein g	42
Sodium mg	345

Ingredients:

- 2 Scoops Chocolate Protein Powder
- 2 TBS Whipping Cream
- 1 Tsp. Mint Extract

Chocolate Thinner Mint	
Servings	1
	Per Serving
Calories	360
Fat g	16
Saturated Fat g	7
Cholesterol mg	70
Carbohydrates g	10
Fiber g	2
Sugar g	4
Protein g	40
Sodium mg	350

Ingredients:
- 2 Scoops Chocolate Protein Powder
- 1 TBS Peanut Butter

Peanut Butter Cup	
Servings	1
	Per Serving
Calories	355
Fat g	14
Saturated Fat g	2
Cholesterol mg	30
Carbohydrates g	14
Fiber g	3
Sugar g	5
Protein g	44
Sodium mg	408

Ingredients:

- 2 Scoops Chocolate Protein Powder
- 1 Cup Frozen Strawberries
- 2 TBS Whipping Cream

Chocolate-Covered Strawberries	
Servings	1
	Per Serving
Calories	437
Fat g	16
Saturated Fat g	7
Cholesterol mg	70
Carbohydrates g	30
Fiber g	7
Sugar g	14
Protein g	41
Sodium mg	355

Chocolate-Covered Banana

Ingredients:
- 2 Scoops Protein Powder
- 1 Banana
- 2 TBS Whipping Cream

Chocolate-Covered Banana	
Servings	1
	Per Serving
Calories	465
Fat g	16
Saturated Fat g	7
Cholesterol mg	70
Carbohydrates g	37
Fiber g	5
Sugar g	18
Protein g	41
Sodium mg	351

French Silk Pie

Ingredients:
- 2 Scoops Chocolate Protein Powder
- 1 Box Fat-Free Instant Pudding
- 2 TBS Whipping Cream

French Silk Pie	
Servings	2
	Per Serving
Calories	280
Fat g	13
Saturated Fat g	7
Cholesterol mg	55
Carbohydrates g	17
Fiber g	1
Sugar g	2
Protein g	20
Sodium mg	330

Chocolate-Covered Cheesecake

Ingredients:
- 2 Scoops Chocolate Protein Powder
- 2 TBS Cream Cheese

Chocolate-Covered Cheesecake	
Servings	1
	Per Serving
Calories	362
Fat g	16
Saturated Fat g	7
Cholesterol mg	59
Carbohydrates g	12
Fiber g	2
Sugar g	5
Protein g	42
Sodium mg	431

Ingredients:

- 2 Scoops Strawberry Protein Powder
- 2 TBS Cream Cheese
- 1 Cup Frozen Strawberries

Strawberry Cheesecake	
Servings	1
	Per Serving
Calories	439
Fat g	16
Saturated Fat g	7
Cholesterol mg	59
Carbohydrates g	32
Fiber g	7
Sugar g	15
Protein g	43
Sodium mg	436

Ingredients:

- 2 Scoops Chocolate Protein Powder
- 2 TBS Whipping Cream
- 6 Ounces Diet Cherry Soda Pop

Chocolate-Covered Cherries	
Servings	1
	Per Serving
Calories	362
Fat g	16
Saturated Fat g	7
Cholesterol mg	59
Carbohydrates g	12
Fiber g	2
Sugar g	5
Protein g	42
Sodium mg	431

Chocolate-Covered Orange

Ingredients:
- 2 Scoops Chocolate Protein Powder
- 2 TBS Whipping Cream
- 6 Ounces Diet Cherry Orange Pop

Chocolate-Covered Orange	
Servings	1
	Per Serving
Calories	362
Fat g	16
Saturated Fat g	7
Cholesterol mg	59
Carbohydrates g	12
Fiber g	2
Sugar g	5
Protein g	42
Sodium mg	431

Cherry Cheesecake

Ingredients:
- 2 Scoops Vanilla Protein Powder
- 2 TBS Cream Cheese
- 6 Ounces Diet Cherry Soda Pop
- 8 Frozen Cherries

Cherry Cheesecake	
Servings	1
	Per Serving
Calories	404
Fat g	16
Saturated Fat g	7
Cholesterol mg	59
Carbohydrates g	22
Fiber g	4
Sugar g	13
Protein g	42
Sodium mg	431

Blueberry Cheesecake

Ingredients:

- 2 Scoops Vanilla Protein Powder
- 2 TBS Cream Cheese
- 1 Cup Frozen Unsweetened Blueberries

Blueberry Cheesecake	
Servings	1
	Per Serving
Calories	442
Fat g	16
Saturated Fat g	7
Cholesterol mg	59
Carbohydrates g	31
Fiber g	6
Sugar g	18
Protein g	43
Sodium mg	433

Cheesecake

Ingredients:
- 2 Scoops Vanilla Protein Powder
- 2 TBS Cream Cheese

Cheesecake	
Servings	1
	Per Serving
Calories	362
Fat g	16
Saturated Fat g	7
Cholesterol mg	59
Carbohydrates g	12
Fiber g	2
Sugar g	5
Protein g	42
Sodium mg	431

Banana Split

Ingredients:
- 2 Scoops Protein Powder
- 1 Banana
- 1 Cup Frozen Strawberries

Banana Split	
Servings	1
	Per Serving
Calories	442
Fat g	6
Saturated Fat g	1
Cholesterol mg	30
Carbohydrates g	57
Fiber g	10
Sugar g	28
Protein g	42
Sodium mg	346

Ingredients:
- ○ 2 Scoops Chocolate Protein Powder
- ○ 2 TBS Marshmallow Fluff
- ○ 1 Graham Cracker

S'Mores	
Servings	1
	Per Serving
Calories	363
Fat g	8
Saturated Fat g	1
Cholesterol mg	30
Carbohydrates g	32
Fiber g	3
Sugar g	15
Protein g	41
Sodium mg	418

PB & J

Ingredients:
- 2 Scoops Protein Powder
- 2 TBS PB 2 (Powdered Peanut Butter)
- 1 Cup Frozen Strawberries

PB&J	
Servings	1
	Per Serving
Calories	387
Fat g	6
Saturated Fat g	1
Cholesterol mg	30
Carbohydrates g	35
Fiber g	9
Sugar g	16
Protein g	46
Sodium mg	415

Chocolate-Covered Raspberries

Ingredients:
- 2 Scoops Protein Powder
- 1/2 Cup Frozen Raspberries
- 1 TBS Whipping Cream

Chocolate-Covered Raspberries	
Servings	1
	Per Serving
Calories	375
Fat g	12
Saturated Fat g	4
Cholesterol mg	30
Carbohydrates g	30
Fiber g	12
Sugar g	12
Protein g	47
Sodium mg	412

Ingredients:

- 2 Scoops Vanilla Protein Powder
- 1/2 Cup Chopped Pineapple
- 1 TBS Whipping Cream
- 2 TBS Shredded Coconut

Piña Colada	
Servings	2
	Per Serving
Calories	247
Fat g	10
Saturated Fat g	4
Cholesterol mg	15
Carbohydrates g	18
Fiber g	2
Sugar g	14
Protein g	21
Sodium mg	171

Ingredients:
- 2 Scoops Vanilla Protein Powder
- 6 Ounces Lime Juice
- 2 TBS Cream Cheese

Key Lime Pie	
Servings	1
	Per Serving
Calories	362
Fat g	16
Saturated Fat g	7
Cholesterol mg	59
Carbohydrates g	12
Fiber g	2
Sugar g	5
Protein g	42
Sodium mg	431

Butterscotch

Ingredients:
- 2 Scoops Vanilla Protein Powder
- 1 Box Fat-Free Butterscotch Pudding

Butterscotch	
Servings	1
	Per Serving
Calories	360
Fat g	6
Saturated Fat g	1
Cholesterol mg	30
Carbohydrates g	35
Fiber g	2
Sugar g	4
Protein g	40
Sodium mg	431

Banana Cream Pie

Ingredients:
- 2 Scoops Vanilla Protein Powder
- 1 Banana
- 1 Graham Cracker

Banana Cream Pie	
Servings	2
	Per Serving
Calories	215
Fat g	4
Saturated Fat g	1
Cholesterol mg	15
Carbohydrates g	25
Fiber g	3
Sugar g	11
Protein g	21
Sodium mg	205

Orange Dream

Ingredients:

- 2 Scoops Vanilla Protein Powder
- 6 Ounces Diet Orange Soda Pop
- 2 TBS Whipping Cream

Orange Dream	
Servings	1
	Per Serving
Calories	360
Fat g	16
Saturated Fat g	9
Cholesterol mg	30
Carbohydrates g	10
Fiber g	2
Sugar g	4
Protein g	40
Sodium mg	345

Mocha Madness

Ingredients:
- 2 Scoops Chocolate Protein Powder
- 1 Cup Chilled Coffee
- 2 TBS Whipping Cream

Mocha Madness	
Servings	1
	Per Serving
Calories	360
Fat g	16
Saturated Fat g	9
Cholesterol mg	30
Carbohydrates g	10
Fiber g	2
Sugar g	4
Protein g	40
Sodium mg	345

French Vanilla Coffee

Ingredients:
- 2 Scoops Vanilla Protein Powder
- 1 Cup Chilled Coffee
- 2 TBS Whipping Cream

French Vanilla Coffee	
Servings	1
	Per Serving
Calories	360
Fat g	16
Saturated Fat g	9
Cholesterol mg	30
Carbohydrates g	10
Fiber g	2
Sugar g	4
Protein g	40
Sodium mg	345

White Chocolate

Ingredients:
- 2 Scoops Vanilla Protein Powder
- 1 Box Fat-Free White Chocolate Instant Pudding

White Chocolate Servings	1
	Per Serving
Calories	360
Fat g	6
Saturated Fat g	1
Cholesterol mg	30
Carbohydrates g	35
Fiber g	2
Sugar g	4
Protein g	40
Sodium mg	650

Ingredients:
- 2 Scoops Vanilla Protein Powder
- 8 Ounces Diet Root Beer Soda Pop
- 2 TBS Whipping Cream

Root Beer Float	
Servings	1
	Per Serving
Calories	360
Fat g	16
Saturated Fat g	9
Cholesterol mg	30
Carbohydrates g	10
Fiber g	2
Sugar g	4
Protein g	40
Sodium mg	345

Lemon Lime Fluff

Ingredients:
- 2 Scoops Vanilla Protein Powder
- 2 Cups Sugar-Free Lemon Lime Jell-O
- 2 TBS Whipping Cream

Lemon Lime Fluff	
Servings	1
	Per Serving
Calories	380
Fat g	16
Saturated Fat g	9
Cholesterol mg	30
Carbohydrates g	10
Fiber g	2
Sugar g	4
Protein g	44
Sodium mg	345

Ingredients:
- 2 Scoops Vanilla Protein Powder
- 2 Cups Sugar-Free Strawberry Banana Jell-O
- 2 TBS Whipping Cream

Strawberry Banana Fluff	
Servings	1
	Per Serving
Calories	380
Fat g	16
Saturated Fat g	9
Cholesterol mg	30
Carbohydrates g	10
Fiber g	2
Sugar g	4
Protein g	44
Sodium mg	345

Ingredients:

- 2 Scoops Vanilla Protein Powder
- 2 Cups Sugar-Free Peach Jell-O
- 2 TBS Whipping Cream
- 1/2 Fresh Peach

Georgia Peach Fluff	
Servings	1
	Per Serving
Calories	448
Fat g	16
Saturated Fat g	9
Cholesterol mg	30
Carbohydrates g	27
Fiber g	5
Sugar g	19
Protein g	46
Sodium mg	345

Berry Cherry

Ingredients:

- 2 Scoops Vanilla Protein Powder
- 2 Cups Sugar-Free Cherry Jell-O
- 2 TBS Whipping Cream

Berry Cherry	
Servings	1
	Per Serving
Calories	380
Fat g	16
Saturated Fat g	9
Cholesterol mg	30
Carbohydrates g	10
Fiber g	2
Sugar g	4
Protein g	44
Sodium mg	345

Candy Cane

Ingredients:
- 2 Scoops Vanilla Protein Powder
- 4 drops Peppermint Extract
- 2 TBS Whipping Cream

Candy Cane	
Servings	1
	Per Serving
Calories	380
Fat g	16
Saturated Fat g	9
Cholesterol mg	30
Carbohydrates g	10
Fiber g	2
Sugar g	4
Protein g	44
Sodium mg	345

Chocolate Candy Cane

Ingredients:

- 2 Scoops Chocolate Protein Powder
- 4 drops Peppermint Extract
- 2 TBS Whipping Cream

Chocolate Candy Cane	
Servings	1
	Per Serving
Calories	380
Fat g	16
Saturated Fat g	9
Cholesterol mg	30
Carbohydrates g	10
Fiber g	2
Sugar g	4
Protein g	44
Sodium mg	345

Egg Nog

Ingredients:
- 2 Scoops Vanilla Protein Powder
- Dash of Allspice
- 2 TBS Whipping Cream

Egg Nog	
Servings	1
	Per Serving
Calories	360
Fat g	16
Saturated Fat g	9
Cholesterol mg	30
Carbohydrates g	10
Fiber g	2
Sugar g	4
Protein g	40
Sodium mg	345

German Chocolate Cake

Ingredients:

- 2 Scoops Chocolate Protein Powder
- 2 TBS Shredded Coconut
- 2 TBS Whipping Cream

German Chocolate Cake	
Servings	1
	Per Serving
Calories	420
Fat g	20
Saturated Fat g	13
Cholesterol mg	30
Carbohydrates g	16
Fiber g	2
Sugar g	10
Protein g	40
Sodium mg	345

Snickers

Ingredients:
- 2 Scoops Vanilla Protein Powder
- 2 TBS Peanut Butter
- 1 TBS Honey

Snickers	
Servings	2
	Per Serving
Calories	257
Fat g	11
Saturated Fat g	3
Cholesterol mg	15
Carbohydrates g	18
Fiber g	2
Sugar g	12
Protein g	24
Sodium mg	238

Ingredients:
- 2 Scoops Vanilla Protein Powder
- 2 TBS Peanut Butter
- 2 TBS Marshmallow Fluff

Salted Nut Roll	
Servings	2
	Per Serving
Calories	245
Fat g	11
Saturated Fat g	3
Cholesterol mg	15
Carbohydrates g	14
Fiber g	2
Sugar g	7
Protein g	24
Sodium mg	240

Blueberry Coffee Cake

Ingredients:
- 2 Scoops Vanilla Protein Powder
- 1 Cup Frozen Unsweetened Blueberries
- 1 Tsp. Cinnamon

Blueberry Coffee Cake	
Servings	1
	Per Serving
Calories	339
Fat g	7
Saturated Fat g	1
Cholesterol mg	30
Carbohydrates g	29
Fiber g	6
Sugar g	17
Protein g	41
Sodium mg	342

Ingredients:

- 2 Scoops Strawberry Protein Powder
- 1 Cup Frozen Strawberries
- 1 Tsp. Cinnamon

Strawberry Coffee Cake	
Servings	1
	Per Serving
Calories	337
Fat g	7
Saturated Fat g	1
Cholesterol mg	30
Carbohydrates g	30
Fiber g	7
Sugar g	14
Protein g	41
Sodium mg	345

Ingredients:
- 2 Scoops Vanilla Protein Powder
- 1 Cup Frozen Peach Slices
- 1 Tsp. Cinnamon

Peach Coffee Cake	
Servings	1
	Per Serving
Calories	320
Fat g	6
Saturated Fat g	1
Cholesterol mg	30
Carbohydrates g	25
Fiber g	4
Sugar g	17
Protein g	41
Sodium mg	340

Morning Glory Muffin

Ingredients:

- 2 Scoops Vanilla Protein Powder
- 1 Cup Frozen Unsweetened Blueberries
- 2 Tsp. Orange Peel Zest
- 1 Tsp. Cinnamon

Morning Glory Muffin	
Servings	1
	Per Serving
Calories	339
Fat g	7
Saturated Fat g	1
Cholesterol mg	30
Carbohydrates g	29
Fiber g	6
Sugar g	17
Protein g	41
Sodium mg	342

Joyful Almond

Ingredients:
- 2 Scoops Vanilla Protein Powder
- 2 TBS Shredded Coconut
- 6 Almonds

Joyful Almond	
Servings	1
	Per Serving
Calories	418
Fat g	17
Saturated Fat g	5
Cholesterol mg	30
Carbohydrates g	26
Fiber g	4
Sugar g	17
Protein g	43
Sodium mg	350

Ingredients:
- 2 Honey Crisp Apples
- 12 Ounces Almond Milk
- 4 Scoops Vanilla Protein Powder
- 1 Tsp. Cinnamon to taste
- 2 Tsp. Nutmeg
- 12 Ice Cubes

Place all ingredients in a blender. Blend, enjoy and use your favorite cup, mug, or glass and make it special because you are worth it.

Apple Pie Protein Shake	
Servings	8
	Per Serving
Calories	99
Fat g	2
Saturated Fat g	0
Cholesterol mg	8
Carbohydrates g	10
Fiber g	2
Sugar g	7
Protein g	10
Sodium mg	88

Snacks

Celery and Peanut Butter

Ingredients:
- 9 Stalks of Celery
- 3 TBS Peanut Butter

Wash, trim and cut celery. Use a spoon or butter knife to spread peanut butter on cut stalks.

Celery and Peanut Butter	
Servings	3
	Per Serving
Calories	116
Fat g	8
Saturated Fat g	1
Cholesterol mg	0
Carbohydrates g	9
Fiber g	3
Sugar g	4
Protein g	5
Sodium mg	170

Squash or Pumpkin Seed Recipe

DID YOU KNOW YOU CAN eat the seeds from more than just pumpkin? Well, you can. Here is a great seed recipe for squash seeds.

Ingredients:

- 4 TBS Squash Seeds (or Pumpkin)
- 1 TBS Olive Oil
- Kosher Coarse Salt to Taste
- Pepper to Taste

Preheat the oven to 250F. Line a baking sheet with parchment paper or aluminum foil. After removing the seeds from the squash, rinse with water and remove any strings and bits of squash. Pat dry and place in a small bowl. Stir the olive oil and salt into the seeds until evenly coated. Spread out in an even layer on the prepared baking sheet. Bake for 15 minutes or until seeds start to pop. Remove from oven and cool on the baking sheet before serving. Top with favorite spices, seasoning or salt.

Squash or Pumpkin Seed Recipe	
Servings	2
	Per Serving
Calories	172
Fat g	9
Saturated Fat g	2
Cholesterol mg	0
Carbohydrates g	2
Fiber g	1
Sugar g	0
Protein g	6
Sodium mg	0

Apple Cinnamon Fun

Ingredients:
- 4 Apples
- 1 TBS Pure Ground Cinnamon
- 2 TBS Brown Sugar (Substitute Brown Sugar made from Stevia)

Wash, peel and core the apples. Quarter the apples. Place on a plate. Then dust with pure ground cinnamon and brown sugar (take the carbs down further by using stevia, splenda, etcetera).

Apple Cinnamon Fun	
Servings	4
	Per Serving
Calories	86
Fat g	1
Saturated Fat g	0
Cholesterol mg	0
Carbohydrates g	24
Fiber g	5
Sugar g	16
Protein g	0
Sodium mg	0

Baked Apple Crunch

Ingredients:
- 4 Apples
- 1 TBS Pure Ground Cinnamon
- 2 TBS Butter
- ½ Cup Quick Oats
- 1/2 cup Stevia Brown Sugar

Wash, peel, core and then slice apples. In a cast-iron frying pan/skillet (you MUST use an oven safe frying pan/skillet) melt butter. Preheat oven to 350F. Toss the apple slices in the butter. Then top with the oats, 1 TBS cinnamon and the brown sugar. Toss and make sure the apples are all coated really well with butter and the spices. Place the cast-iron skillet into the oven for 20-25 minutes. Remove, toss and serve. This recipe is incredible. For those wanting to watch carbs or macros more closely, cut out the oats and make sure to use a sugar-free or stevia brown sugar.

Baked Apple Crunch	
Servings	4
	Per Serving
Calories	174
Fat g	7
Saturated Fat g	4
Cholesterol mg	15
Carbohydrates g	30
Fiber g	6
Sugar g	16
Protein g	1
Sodium mg	50

Dipping Sweet Peppers and Ranch

Ingredients:
- 2-4 Sweet Peppers
- Light or Low-Calorie Ranch Dressing

Wash, core and remove seeds from peppers. Slice peppers into long strips. Pour 1-2 TBS of ranch dressing into the bottom of a glass. If you slice the peppers creatively, they will hang on the side of the glass.

Dipping Sweet Peppers and Ranch	
Servings	2
	Per Serving
Calories	168
Fat g	11
Saturated Fat g	2
Cholesterol mg	0
Carbohydrates g	18
Fiber g	2
Sugar g	9
Protein g	2
Sodium mg	289

Crust-Free Pizza

Ingredients:
- 6 Mozzarella Cheese Sticks (String Cheese)
- 1 Cup Pasta Sauce

Open string cheese and remove from their package. Pour sauce in a small bowl. Dip cheese sticks and enjoy.

Crust-Free Pizza	
Servings	2
	Per Serving
Calories	325
Fat g	20
Saturated Fat g	11
Cholesterol mg	66
Carbohydrates g	15
Fiber g	3
Sugar g	11
Protein g	21
Sodium mg	1014

Zucchini Chips

Ingredients:
- ○ 2 Zucchini
- ○ 1 TBS Olive Oil
- ○ Salt
- ○ Paprika

Cut zucchini into thin slices and toss in 1 TBS olive oil, sea salt and pepper. Sprinkle with paprika and bake at 450F for 25 to 30 minutes. Use paprika not only to flavor this healthy snack, but also to boost your metabolism, reduce your appetite and lower your blood pressure.

Zucchini Chips	
Servings	4
	Per Serving
Calories	47
Fat g	4
Saturated Fat g	1
Cholesterol mg	0
Carbohydrates g	3
Fiber g	1
Sugar g	2
Protein g	1
Sodium mg	3

Dips, Condiments, Toppings and Seasonings

Red Pepper Hummus

Ingredients:
- 2 Cloves of Garlic
- 1 Can Garbanzo Beans
- 4 TBS Tahini
- 1 TBS Olive Oil
- 1/3 Cup Lemon Juice
- 1/2 Cup Roasted Red Peppers
- 1/4 Tsp. Basil

Drain beans and add to food processor. Press garlic and add to food processor. Add each of the other ingredients one at a time, running the food processor after each one.

Red Pepper Hummus	
Servings	4
	Per Serving
Calories	223
Fat g	14
Saturated Fat g	2
Cholesterol mg	0
Carbohydrates g	20
Fiber g	5
Sugar g	4
Protein g	7
Sodium mg	162

Ingredients:
- 2 Ripe Avocados
- 3 TBS Lime Juice
- 3/4 Tsp. Kosher Salt
- 1/2 Tsp. Ground Coriander (optional; if you do not have it skip it!)
- 1/2 Tsp. Cumin
- 4 TBS Chopped Cilantro

Halve the avocados, pit them and scoop the flesh with a large spoon into a small mixing bowl. Pour lime juice over the avocados, add the salt, coriander and cumin and use a spoon to break up the avocados, stirring until they're coarsely mashed. Stir in 3 TBS. of the cilantro. Taste and add more lime juice, cilantro and salt as needed.

Guacamole. Most of the time when we hear that we think…chips, salsa, great Mexican food, an ice-cold Corona and maybe a margarita. What we do not think of is a condiment. Guacamole is a great healthy fat replacement for things like mayo. Try it on a sandwich or a wrap. How about on a burger or chicken breast?

Homemade Guacamole Recipe	
Servings	4
	Per Serving
Calories	114
Fat g	11
Saturated Fat g	2
Cholesterol mg	0
Carbohydrates g	6
Fiber g	5
Sugar g	0
Protein g	1
Sodium mg	6

Baja Mango Salsa

Ingredients:
- 3 Mangos
- 2 Roma Tomatoes
- 1 Bunch Cilantro
- 1 Fresh Lemon
- 1 Fresh Lime
- Pink Himalayan Salt

Wash everything. Dice the mangos and tomatoes. Chop the cilantro. Quarter the lemon and lime. Combine everything in a large bowl and squeeze juice from lemons and limes over the top. Toss and then let sit overnight in the refrigerator. Use as a topping on chicken or fish tacos. Can also be used with tortilla chips in place of regular salsa.

Baja Mango Salsa	
Servings	4
	Per Serving
Calories	109
Fat g	0
Saturated Fat g	0
Cholesterol mg	0
Carbohydrates g	30
Fiber g	3
Sugar g	23
Protein g	1
Sodium mg	5

High-Protein Ranch Dip

Ingredients:

- 1 Packet Ranch Dip Mix
- 4 Cups Plain Greek Yogurt (Low-Fat lowers calories)
- 2 TBS Sour Cream

Mix 2 TBS of sour cream into a container of plain Greek yogurt. Add packet of ranch dip mix. Dip your favorite fresh vegetables in and enjoy!

High-Protein Ranch Dip	
Servings	4
	Per Serving
Calories	208
Fat g	6
Saturated Fat g	4
Cholesterol mg	35
Carbohydrates g	13
Fiber g	1
Sugar g	5
Protein g	12
Sodium mg	734

Italian Vinaigrette

Ingredients:

- ○ 1 TBS Olive Oil
- ○ 2 TBS Balsamic Vinegar
- ○ 1 Tsp. Oregano
- ○ 1 Tsp. Basil

Combine all ingredients in a small container and or bowl.

Italian Vinaigrette	
Servings	1
	Per Serving
Calories	150
Fat g	14
Saturated Fat g	2
Cholesterol mg	0
Carbohydrates g	8
Fiber g	0
Sugar g	4
Protein g	0
Sodium mg	0

Ingredients:

- 1 Packet Taco Seasoning
- 4 Cups Low-Fat Plain Greek Yogurt
- 2 TBS Sour Cream

Mix 2 TBS of sour cream in container of plain Greek yogurt. Add packet of taco seasoning. Dip your favorite fresh vegetables in and enjoy!

High-Protein Taco Dip	
Servings	4
	Per Serving
Calories	215
Fat g	6
Saturated Fat g	4
Cholesterol mg	35
Carbohydrates g	15
Fiber g	1
Sugar g	5
Protein g	12
Sodium mg	704

Make Your Own Taco Seasoning

Ingredients:

- 1 TBS Chili Powder
- 2 Tsp. Paprika
- 1 Tsp. Onion Powder
- ½ Tsp. Salt
- ½ Tsp. Garlic Powder
- ½ Tsp. Ground Cumin
- ½ Tsp. Oregano
- ¼ Tsp. Black Pepper
- 1 Pinch Cayenne Pepper (optional)
- 1 Pinch Red Pepper Flakes (optional)

Combine in bowl and mix.

Make Your Own Taco Seasoning	
Servings	4
	Per Serving
Calories	12
Fat g	0
Saturated Fat g	0
Cholesterol mg	0
Carbohydrates g	1
Fiber g	0
Sugar g	0
Protein g	0
Sodium mg	59

Made in the USA
Columbia, SC
30 May 2019